MODERN SEA POWER

BERNARD BRETT

WHSMITH
EXCLUSIVE ·BOOKS·

Photographic acknowledgments

The Publishers and TRH Pictures would like to thank the Royal Navy, United States Navy, Merchant Navy and the many companies who have helped with the preparation of this book.

Aérospatiale, Paris, 234; Associated Press, London, 230/231; Barr & Stroud, Glasgow, 122; BBC Central Stills Library, London, 220, 224–225, 226–227, 244–245, 246–247, 250–251; Ben Lines, London, 100–101; British Aerospace, London, 47, 122; Cammell Laird/Williamson Art Gallery, Birkenhead, 80, 100–101, 105; Department of Defense, Washington D.C., 50–51, 175, 176–177, 182–183, 214; Fleet Air Arm Museum, Yeovilton, 63; General Dynamics, Pomona, 197; Grumman Aerospace, Long Island, 46 bottom, 68–69; HMS *Warrior* Trust, Hartlepool, 9, 10; *Illustrated London News*, London, 82–83; Imperial War Museum, London, 15, 16, 18, 19, 20–21, 42–43, 49, 54–55 top, 54–55 bottom, 71, 87, top, 87 bottom, 152, 153, 154, 155, 156–157, 164–165, 165; Lockheed Missiles, California, 146–147; Marconi Defence Systems, Stanmore, 196; Marconi Undersea, Waterlooville, 130; Mary Evans Picture Library, London, 85; McDonnell Douglas, St. Louis 143; NATO, London, 7; National Archives, Washington D.C., 17, 178; Norwegian Caribbean, 94–95; P & O, London, 88, 89, 90–91, 95, 96–97, 108–109, 242–243; OCL, London, 116; Oto Melara Spa, La Spezia, 127; Plessey, London, 195; Racal Decca, London, 102–103, 110–111, 112 top, 112 bottom, 113 bottom, 114, 115; Royal Fleet Auxiliary, London, 218–219, 219, 222–223, 228, 240; Royal Navy, 64, 76, 141 top, 141 bottom, 169, 184–185, 198–199, 202, 204–205, 206, 207, 221, 229, 232–233, 237, 238–239, 241, 248–249, 253 top, 252–253; Scicon, London, 131; Smithsonian Institute, Washington D.C., 45; Thomas Cook/*Illustrated London News*, London, 79, 84; Thomson CSF, Paris, 124 bottom; TRH Pictures, 73, 97, 113 top, 125, 132; United States Navy, 6, 12–13, 23, 25 bottom, 34–35, 36–37, 36 bottom, 38–39, 40–41, 44, 46 top, 46 centre, 52–53, 56–57, 58–59, 59, 60–61, 62, 65, 66–67, 67, 70, 72, 74–75, 77 bottom, 106–107, 107, 117, 118, 119, 120, 123, 124 top, 126, 128, 129, 133, 134, 135, 136–137, 137, 138–139, 142, 148, 151 bottom, 151 top, 158–159, 160–161, 162, 163, 166, 168–169, 170, 171, 172–173, 174, 181, 186–187, 188, 189, 190–191, 192–193, 200, 201, 203, 204–205, 208, 209, 210, 210–211, 212–213, 215, 216–217; United States Naval Historic Center, Washington D.C., 11, 25 top, 26–27, 28, 29, 30–31, 32–33, 46–47, 48, 150; Victoria and Albert Museum, London, 14; Vickers, Barrow, 236; Yarrow Shipbuilders, Glasgow, 193, 194.

Front cover: Top to bottom, left to right: French Navy Suffren class destroyer (D602), 1983 (SIRPA – Marine Nationale/MARS, Lincolnshire; NATO exercise in Atalantic off coast of Virginia (Colorific, London); *Redoubtable*, French Navy's nuclear-powered ballistic missile submarine (SIRPA-Navale/MARS, Lincolnshire); USS *Iowa* firing 16-in guns off battleship's portside during operations in Western Caribbean 1984 (TRH Pictures, London); HMS *Broadsword* (F-88), Broadsword class frigate, Royal Navy (Crown Copyright HMS *Osprey*/MARS, Lincolnshire)

Back cover: USS *John F Kennedy* (CV-67), John Kennedy class carrier in the Atlantic, 1978 (U.S. Navy/MARS, Lincolnshire)

Titlespread: U.S. nuclear attack submarine (Colorific, London)

**This edition produced exclusively for
W H Smith**

Published by
The Hamlyn Publishing Group Limited
London · New York · Sydney · Toronto
Bridge House, Twickenham, Middlesex TW1 3SB, England

Copyright © The Hamlyn Publishing Group Limited 1986
ISBN 0 603 03899 9

Printed in Italy

Contents

THE ERA OF THE BATTLESHIP

Sea power, the attempt to gain control of the seas, is as old as the ship itself. The merchant fleets of the ancient Mediterranean civilizations, especially those of Crete, sought to establish great trading empires, carrying their goods to every point of the compass, founding colonies and creating settlements. These slow ponderous merchantmen, wallowing across the Mediterranean under sail alone, were easy prey for swift, oar-propelled pirate galleys that were quick to snatch such rich defenceless prizes. To protect them trading states built fleets of military vessels manned by sea-soldiers, and thus laid the foundations for one of the cardinal principles of modern sea power – the necessity for countries dependent for survival on imports to protect their mercantile marine. Later, as these Mediterranean fleets became more powerful, they were used to support or repel the invading armies of ambitious states seeking to dominate the area, another principle of sea power that still remains valid today. Unfortunately the enforcement of sea power is no longer restricted to such simple elements; over the centuries other considerations have crept in, until nowadays the control of the seas and the manipulation of fleets has become a highly charged political exercise with many facets to be considered. No more is the role of a navy simply to engage an enemy fleet; sea power is now intrinsically interwoven with land and air forces to create an integrated power structure.

Opposite: USS New Jersey in dock for a refit.

Below: Ships of NATO's Standing Naval Forces Atlantic (STANAVFORLANT) on station in the Atlantic. The need to keep the Atlantic sea lanes secure against submarine attack is as important today as ever.

There are many aspects and as many definitions of sea power. To many the phrase conjures up a picture of a battle fleet majestically ploughing its way line-ahead through a heaving sea, spray enveloping its mighty 15-in guns. In fact, the warship only fully comes into its own during a time of war; its peacetime role is restricted to that of a political deterrent, described by Mahan as the 'silent pressure of sea power', plus additional minor duties. The commercial use of the sea is far more important, even if it lacks the romantic appeal of roaring guns. Great sea powers, trading empires with easy access to the sea, have arisen because of their geographical position, the excellence of their harbours and ports, the availability of overseas bases and development of trade throughout the world. It is only when these are threatened that warships begin to play a more important role.

Ships and War

Two former definitions of maritime strategy are still valid today but in the broader sense of an integrated military strategy combining land, sea and air forces: Admiral Richmond defined it as 'the art of concentrating the utmost force at the right time and place'; General Beaufre claimed it was 'the art of employing force towards political ends'. With the advent of, first, the aeroplane and, in more recent times, the nuclear-armed, intercontinental guided missile, the following claim made by a naval planner in the heyday of the battleship has a hollow ring to it – but its main point is still valid, especially in the case of a small island state such as the United Kingdom: 'The Navy is first, second, third, fourth, fifth – ad infinitum Line of Defence! If the Navy is not supreme, no army, however large, is of the slightest use. It is not invasion we have to fear if our Navy is beaten, it's *starvation*.' The U-Boat arm of the German *Kriegsmarine* all but proved this point during its extremely significant all-out campaigns against the vitally important Allied merchant shipping in the two world wars.

Although bomber aircraft and the guided missile have totally altered the concept of naval warfare, their introduction has augmented rather than diminished the principles of maritime strategy which may be defined as follows:

1. To engage and either destroy or cripple an enemy fleet.

2. By blockade or other means to prevent an enemy fleet threatening sea communication.

3. To effect the economic life of an enemy by attacking his mercantile marine.

4. To protect a country's own mercantile marine.

5. To prevent invasion by sea.

6. To provide out-flanking and diversionary movements (and keep them supplied) to assist in a decisive result on land.

7. To offer defence to other warships operating within range of submarines, bomber aircraft or missiles.

8. To act as an instrument of state power and policy.

Since early days naval tactics have been determined by the most powerful weapon in existence at the time, although basic principles have remained constant. Until well into the 20th century naval tactics were also governed by the horizon – the enemy had to be in sight before a naval engagement could take place and intelligence was obtained by employing fast reconnaissance warships. The aeroplane and missile have changed all that; now, with the aid of sophisticated radar techniques, warships, often hundreds of miles apart, can engage in battle without ever seeing one another.

It was the introduction of cannon into naval warfare in the Middle Ages that first altered the pattern of fighting at sea and led to the evolution of the monster battleship which was, for a short time, the epitome of naval power. Before then tactics were simple and unsophisticated: warships attempted either to ram each other or to come alongside to allow sea-going infantry to board and carry the fight to the enemy. At first cannon were light 'man-killing' pieces mounted in the fore and aft 'castles' and deployed to fire downwards into the enemy as they scrambled aboard. Gradually these guns increased in size until they were able to inflict considerable damage on the ships themselves and not just their crews, although being so stoutly built, ships were rarely sunk by gunfire alone. Of the 130 ships comprising the Spanish Armada of 1588, only two were sunk and one of those blew up. Even as late as Napoleonic times, 'first rates' had to batter away at point-blank range to have any effect on the

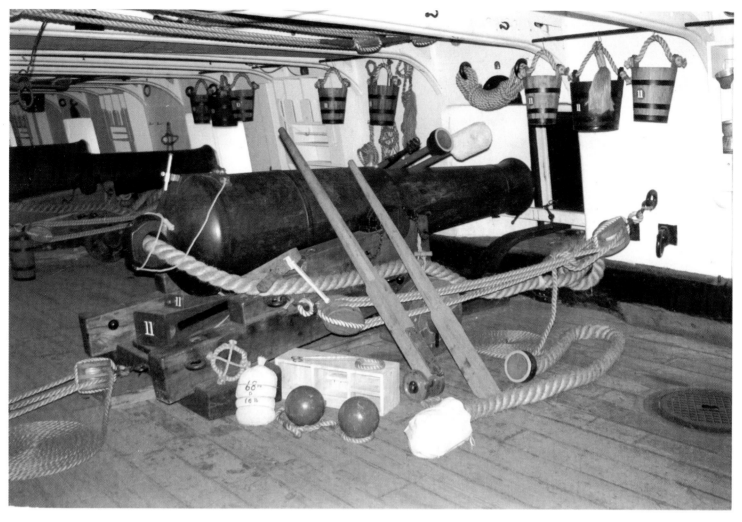

enemy. At any distance, even the heaviest 42-lb (18-kg) shot had little effect on the 18-in (46-cm) thick timbers of a 'ship-of-the-line', and 'grappling' and boarding tactics were still employed.

It was following the Napoleonic Wars that the first step was taken towards the evolution of the modern battleship. Smarting after its defeat at the hands of the British, the French Navy, a virtually spent force with a three-to-one disadvantage in ships, realized that even the most ambitious shipbuilding programme would not bring it to terms equal to the Royal Navy. What was required was a revolutionary new weapon, one that would cancel out France's lack of ships. An artillery officer, General Henri Paixhans, supplied the answer – the shell gun. The shell, in itself, was not new; Nelson had used such hollow iron spheres filled with gunpowder and fitted with a delayed-action fuse to great effect at Copenhagen, but he had fired them from squat mortars which rendered them inaccurate at any great range. What Paixhans did was to adapt the shell so that it could be fired from a 'long' ship gun; this modification, he claimed, would make the

wooden ship obsolete, for a shell exploding inside the hull would most likely set the ship ablaze if not detonate the magazine. At Sinope in 1853, the Russian Black Sea Fleet, firing such shells, completely annihilated – sinking every ship – a Turkish fleet of wooden ships firing only solid shot.

To counter the effect of the explosive shell, navies turned to cladding the wooden hulls of their warships with iron, thus producing a stalemate. In the very first engagement between two ironclads which occurred during the American Civil War, USS *Monitor* registered 20 direct hits with her 11-in Dahlgrens; CSS *Merrimack* 23 direct hits with her 9-in Dahlgrens. Although fired at point-blank range, the ships often all but touching, neither sets of guns inflicted any lasting damage, or for that matter managed to penetrate the hull of the enemy. Once the introduction of steam gave warships total manoeuvrability independent of wind conditions, the race was on between bigger and more powerful naval guns and increasingly thicker, more protective armour.

The introduction of an efficient breech-loading system speeded up the rate of fire by

A 68-pounder muzzle-loader aboard HMS Warrior, 1860, with her loading tools, types of shot and recoil tackle. The Warrior was armed with both muzzle-loaders and the new breech-loaders.

This 110-pounder, mounted on HMS Warrior, was the first rifle-barrelled breech-loader to enter service with the Royal Navy. She was built in reply to the French ironclad La Gloire, built in 1859.

eliminating the need to bring the muzzle-loaders inboard each time to reload; and the advent of slow-burning gunpowder in 1870 increased the muzzle velocity of the shell giving it greater power of penetration. As shells reached a monstrous 18 in in calibre (for instance, the Italian battleship *Duilio*, laid down in 1872, carried four 17.7-in guns), the main armour of a ship increased to as much as 24 in (61 cm) thick. However, the era of these heavy guns was short-lived for their disadvantages soon became apparent. Not only were they slow to fire – the *Duilio* could fire only one gun at a time to avoid serious structural damage, and HMS *Inflexible*, considered a fast-firer at the time, could manage only one round every two minutes – but they were also inaccurate and the effect of their blast threatened to do their own ship more harm than they could inflict on the enemy.

Rise of the Modern Battleship

By the last decade of the 19th century these problems had been resolved and the modern battleship was well on its way.

More effective gunnery and gun design enabled heavy armament to be reduced in size to a more or less standard calibre of 12 in (25 cm). Quick firing from hydraulically controlled turrets enabled these guns to deliver a considerable volume of shell in heavy broadsides and this proved more effectively damaging than a few rounds of a heavier calibre. Naval theorists were well aware that the increasing efficiency of gunnery and gun design would force battles at sea to be fought at increasing ranges, but without practical experience it had to remain just theory. [However, as theory became fact ranges increased. In 1860 a range of 1,000 yd (900 m) was the norm; by 1880 it had increased to 2,000 yd (1,800 m) and at the turn of the century to 6,000 yd (5,500 m). By the beginning of the First World War, the figure was 18,000 yd (16,500 m).]

Furthermore, as the positive aspects of using phosphorous in steel-making became fully appreciated, hardened steel, produced more cheaply, reduced the thickness of main armour to 12 in (30 cm), thereby giving the battleship an added turn of speed.

The maritime nations of Europe – in the north and Atlantic mainly Great Britain, France, Russia and in the Mediterranean, Italy – kept a jealous eye on each other, either copying or improving on gun design and control, power units, or armour. Great Britain kept a two-power standard, its navy equalling in strength the combined fleets of any two other countries, which, until 1898, meant France and Russia. In that year, Germany, passing the first of its Naval Laws, threw itself into an ambitious shipbuilding programme which Germany claimed would make it the second strongest naval power in Europe in little more than a decade. This decision provoked an arms race among the European maritime powers, anxious to keep ahead of the emerging rival in both number and quality of battleships. Although the need for Japan and the United States to compete was less pressing, they nonetheless kept a wary eye on the developments in Europe, and both were to play a considerable part in the development of the battleship: Japan by putting theory into practice in the first modern naval engagement, and the United States by the calm way it set out to determine the best method of protecting battleships against long-range gunfire – the 'zone of immunity' theory. The European arms race, however, proved to be of little benefit, for within a very few years the 'all-big-gun' battleship the mighty HMS *Dreadnought* was to make all the rest of the world's capital ships obsolete.

THE RISE OF THE BATTLESHIP

Country	Name	Speed in Knots	Launch Date	Displacement		Length		Armament	Armour
				tons	tonnes	feet	metres		
Great Britain	*Warrior*	14	1869	9,000	9,100	367	112	26 68-pounders 10 110-pounders 4 70-pounders	1,200 tons (1,200 tonnes)
Italy	*Andrea Doria*	16	1885	11,200	11,400	328.2	100.0	4 45.0-cm	Armoured Citadel 22-in
Great Britain	*Revenge*	17.5	1892	14,150	14,400	380	116	4 13.5-in 12 6-in 16 6-pounders	Turrets 17-in

The Italian Andrea Doria under construction at La Spezia. Launched in 1885, she was armed with four 17-in guns and had a top speed of 16 knots; she was to cause consternation among the navies of the world.

At the turn of the century, until oil-fired boilers were installed in battleships, overseas bases played an important part in sea power. Navies with worldwide commitments, such as Great Britain with her Empire, were dependent on plentiful, strategically positioned coal supplies. Germany, on the other hand, possessed a continental navy and was able to supply coal from home bases. However, from the very beginning of the First World War, her cruiser warfare was curtailed and finally halted as the number of her coaling bases diminished, falling one by one to the Allies.

Coaling a battleship was a filthy task hated by everyone aboard ship, except, oddly enough, the stokers. Normally stokers toiled in fierce heat, trapped below decks in a gloomy, ill-lit stokehold which reeked of burnt-out furnaces, coal dust and grease and which were battened down during action. They earned the right to lounge about on deck while the rest of the ship's company took on the coal.

As soon as the collier came alongside, orders were shouted and the crew, muttering and cursing, set up derricks, made ready the winches, removed the covers of the circular coal hatches and rigged up the shutes which reached from deck to deck down to the coal bunkers. In theory the shutes, two halves clamped together, kept the coal dust from flying over the mess decks; in practice they were a total failure. Unfortunately they lost shape; the joints and fittings became distorted by being roughly hammered together and coal dust would squirt through gaps and cracks covering the whole ship in a grimy black film. Two hundredweight (51-kg) coal sacks, filled in the collier, were winched aboard, wheeled to the shutes on barrows and tipped. Black-faced, enveloped in an all-pervading fog of coal dust, the disgruntled crew would continue this back-breaking chore until the ship's bunkers were filled; sometimes well over 1,000 tons (1,020 tonnes) would be taken aboard, the best part of a day's work — then followed the misery of cleaning ship.

At the order to clean ship, the whole ship's company would turn-to with mops, brooms and wet cloths to wash away the coal dust that penetrated into every crevice in the ship. Nowhere was exempt, from the captain's cabin on a battleship to crew's galleys.

American stokers at work in the stokehold of a coal-fired warship. It was a dirty and back-breaking job.

The *Dreadnought*

Object lessons learned from the Battle of Tsushima during the Russo-Japanese War of 1904 vindicated the British reasoning behind the construction of HMS *Dreadnought*, a revolutionary concept in capital ship design, the first truly modern battleship. When the Japanese Admiral Togo massacred Admiral Rojdestvenky's fleet, sinking 22 of his 37 ships including six of his eight battleships (the other two surrendered), a number of important points emerged from the engagement. Taking his six battleships across the course of the Russian fleet approaching line-ahead (a manoeuvre called 'Crossing the T'), Togo opened fire with a full broadside from his main armament of 12-in and 10-in guns at an unprecedented 7,000 yd (6,400 m), with devastating effect. At this range secondary armament proved useless; one eyewitness remarked, 'for all the respect they instil, 8-in or 6-in guns might just as well be peashooters'. What was more, at that range all shell splashes looked alike and it was impossible to spot individual fire. Another vital factor at Tsushima was the enormous advantage gained by the Japanese because of the superior speed of their ships.

The *Dreadnought*, already on the stocks in Portsmouth Dockyard at the time of the battle, 28 May 1905, had anticipated all the lessons to be gleaned from it, and set the pattern for all subsequent battleships right up to the 72,000-ton (73,000-tonne) Japanese monsters *Yamato* and *Musashi* of the early 1940s. The *Dreadnought*, built and made ready for sea in only 14 months – a record that still stands – was prompted by an article written by an Italian warship designer, Cuniberti, in which he advocated a 17,000-ton (17,300-tonne) battleship mounting 12 12-in guns and able to reach a speed of 24 knots. Urged on by dynamic autocratic Admiral Sir John Fisher, the First Sea Lord, the British Committee on Warship Design agreed to build such a ship. The first battleship to be powered by four-shaft Parsons steam turbines, she had a maximum speed of 21 knots and carried only a main armament of ten 12-in guns mounted in five twin turrets.

Opposite: A Japanese warship at the battle of Tsushima in 1905. The heavily gunned Japanese fleet destroyed 22 Russian ships out of a total 37.

HMS *Dreadnought*	
Displacement	22,000 tons (22,400 tonnes)
Length	561 ft (171 m)
Armament	10 12-in
	24 12-pounders
	5 torpedo tubes
Armour	11-in (28-cm) steel
Speed	21 knots

Below: The clean lines of HMS Dreadnought. Admiral Fisher's concept of the 'Dreadnought' class of ships paved the way for the modern battleship.

By 1915, ships like the 'Super Dreadnought', HMS Queen Elizabeth, had grown to over 30,000 tons (30,500 tonnes) and mounted 15-in guns.

Other countries were not slow to follow the example of Great Britain, and dreadnoughts – the name 'dreadnought' became synonymous with this type of ship – began to slide down the slipways on both sides of the Atlantic and in the Far East. Guns increased in size from 12-in to 13.5-in and finally, in 1915, to 15-in; the seemingly small increase in diameter gave a very large increase in shell weight indeed – 850 lb (385 kg) to 1,400 lb (634 kg) to a vast 1,920 lb (870 kg). As a result of this, battleships also grew in size, their displacement rising dramatically in a very short time: *Dreadnought*, 1905, 22,000 tons (22,400 tonnes); *König*. 1914, 28,150 tons (28,600 tonnes); *Queen Elizabeth*, 1915, 33,000 tons (33,500 tonnes).

The increase in speed was less dramatic, for to raise the speed even one knot above *Dreadnought's* 21 knots required an enormous rise in horsepower: *Dreadnought*, 21 knots with 23,000 main engine horsepower; *Queen Elizabeth*, 24 knots with 75,000 main engine horsepower.

The 'Queen Elizabeth' class were the first battleships to be driven solely by oil, giving not only a greater speed, but a saving in weight that could be taken up by an increase in protective armour. Furthermore, it speeded up refuelling by doing away with the back-breaking chore of coaling ship.

Preparations for War

As ships grew in size and gun power, the naval architect was faced with three inseparable variables: firepower, protective armour and speed. These factors were completely interrelated, a change in one automatically affecting the others. If emphasis was laid on firepower and protective armour, then lower speeds had to be accepted; conversely, higher speeds called for a reduction in weight, either less massive armour, or smaller calibre guns. The bemused naval architect had to juggle with these variables to produce a compromise that would satisfy all, or at least most, critics. Navies usually laid emphasis on one factor or another. The Royal Navy with its overwhelming superiority in battleships, designed to bring the growing menace of a German High Seas Fleet to a pitched battle, concentrated on speed and firepower at the expense of armour. The Germans, on the other hand, took a much more defensive line – though they strenuously denied it at the time – sacrificing hitting power and speed for greater protective armour.

An added factor in battleship design was the cubic capacity (volume) and weight taken up by living accommodation aboard, and the vast storage space required to victual crews of up to 1,500 men. The Royal Navy, required to deploy its ships over the immense distances of the British Empire, was obliged to provide more spacious accommodation for crews than the Germans, who designed their battleships for more localized warfare.

Soon a further complication was added to the already difficult task of the naval architect: the introduction and rapid development of the locomotive torpedo and,

even more telling, the coming of the submarine that could fire it, silent and unseen, from below the waves. The danger from torpedoes fired from fast surface craft, torpedo boats and destroyers, had already been taken into consideration at the outbreak of the First World War, with the re-introduction of quick-firing 6-in (15-cm) secondary armament.

The torpedo itself had become a destructive, lethal weapon. Its initial range of 1,000 yd (900 m) at 7 knots had increased to one of 4,000 yd (3,700 m) at 4 knots or 10,000 yd (9,000 m) at 28 knots. It was quite capable of sinking a battleship if it struck it in a vulnerable spot. Several methods were tried to counter this, but none proved really effective, which led more pessimistic naval prophets to forecast the end of the battleship as the main striking force of a fleet. The majority,

The after-deck heavy guns on the German battleship Kaiser, *commissioned in time for the First World War.*

however, were optimistic and clung to the concept of mighty floating fortresses well into the Second World War, until naval aircraft fully exposed their vulnerability. However, today the U.S. Navy sees a renewed specialized role for the battleship. The underwater danger to the battleship was mitigated to some extent by strengthening the armour belt of the hull, by introducing more internal subdivisions of watertight compartments and by increasing its speed to enable the ship to turn away from the running torpedo. In harbour, battleships were protected by torpedo nets slung from booms.

Until the intervening years between the wars, little attention was paid to the American theory of the 'zone of immunity'. Ignoring the effect of secondary armament, the U.S. designers concentrated on finding a method of protecting their battleships from long-range main armament gunfire, the 'all or nothing' theory. They sought a balance between strengthening side armour as protection against short-range shells fired with a flat trajectory, and deck armour to counter 'plunging' long-range shells. By arguing that there must be some range beyond which a flat trajectory shell would not penetrate the belt armour, and a minimum range outside which a 'plunging' shell would penetrate deck armour, they arrived at a 'zone of immunity'. Within this 'zone of immunity' a battleship could manoeuvre to engage the enemy but be relatively safe from crippling damage.

This called for a nice balance of the three main elements: an over-protected ship would have to compromise on speed and/or armour; an under-protected ship would be highly vulnerable in action, especially one fought at long range. Armour was strengthened in proportion to the importance and vulnerability of the part of the ship to be protected. By and large the heaviest armour was used to protect the ship's vitals, engines and boilers, magazines, main turrets and gunnery controls.

The mighty *Bismarck*, one of the most efficiently armoured ships of the Second World War – she took a tremendous

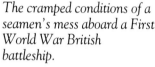

The cramped conditions of a seamen's mess aboard a First World War British battleship.

battering before she finally went under – had an almost perfect distribution of heavy armour. Her armoured belt, running between two transversed bulkheads, 557 ft (170 m) apart – forward of 'A' (Anton) turret to abaft 'D' (Dora) turret – varied in thickness up to 12.5 in (31.8 cm). An armoured deck – a protection against plunging shellfire – ranging in thickness from 3.1 in (7.9 cm) to 4.7 in (11.9 cm), also ran between the same two points. The turrets of the main 15-in (38-cm) armament were mounted with 12.5-in (31.8-cm) armour in front and 8.6-in (21.8 cm) along the sides. The fire-control stations were also heavily armoured. Bismarck's last battle, against two British capital ships and two heavy cruisers which delivered a combined broadside of 20 tons (20 tonnes) of armour-piercing, high explosive shell, against her own broadside of just over 6.5 tons (6.6 tonnes), lasted 90 minutes before she was reduced to a battered hulk. Yet not a single one of the 2,876 shells fired at Bismarck [380 16-in, 339 14-in, 752 8-in, 716 6-in, 660 5.25-in] penetrated the

armour belt or deck, even when the range closed to 2,500 yards (2,300 m). There is some argument as to whether she was finally sunk by three torpedoes fired by the heavy cruiser Dorsetshire or, in fact, scuttled herself. It is certain that Admiral Sir John Tovey, Commander-in-Chief aboard the King George V, signalled Vice-Admiral Sir James Somerville towards the end, 'Cannot get her to sink with guns.'

One glaring instance when naval architects abandoned the nice balance of variables was the battle-cruiser. The Invincible, Inflexible and Indomitable, battle-cruisers completed in 1908, were formidable-looking fighting ships – even their sternest critics admitted that, and there were plenty of those.

Originally known as Dreadnought armoured-cruisers, they were built at the insistence of Admiral Fisher who saw them as a means of making the heavy cruiser obsolete. With a displacement of 17,250 tons (17,530 tonnes), carrying eight 12-in guns and 16 4-in guns, they were designed to keep the trade routes clear of marauding

The battle-cruiser HMS Inflexible, built in 1908, a type of ship that showed its vulnerability to attack from the new generation of warships.

Overleaf: 'The Battle of Jutland', a painting by R.H. Smith. Both sides claimed victory, but the German High Seas Fleet did not risk putting to sea again.

enemy armoured cruisers, who could mount only 8.2-in guns. By doubling the horsepower they could reach speeds of over 25 knots, but all this was achieved at the expense of protective armour. With only a 6-in (15-cm) steel belt amidships, 4 in (10 cm) in the bows and no armoured belt at all abaft the after turret, this hybrid warship was never intended to fight it out with a battleship. Furthermore, her decks, 2-in (5-cm) steel at the thickest point, reducing to 0.75 in (2 cm) in parts, was no protection against the plunging fire of an enemy battleship's main batteries. Fisher argued that her turn of speed – *Invincible* in trials was reported to have bettered 28 knots – would be her protection. But the critics of the battle-cruiser concept saw it differently; one wrote, 'Vessels of this enormous size [the 'Lion' class displaced 29,680 tons (30,155 tonnes)] and cost are unsuitable for many of the duties of cruisers, but an even stronger objection to the repetition of the type is that an admiral having 'Invincibles' in his fleet will be certain to put them in the line of battle, where their comparatively light protection will be a disadvantage and their high speed of no value.' Such proved to be the case, with disastrous results, even against the similarly armed battle-cruisers that other navies were quick to build.

At the Battle of Jutland, the only major fleet engagement of the First World War, three British and one German battle-cruiser were lost, with fearful casualties. Although the Royal Navy's Grand Fleet achieved its object in bringing the whole of the German High Seas Fleet to battle, it failed to annihilate it, or even inflict any appreciable damage; the two fleets spent the rest of the war swinging round their buoys at opposite sides of the North Sea. The German fleet, always a potential threat by its very existence, tied up the main units of the Grand Fleet, and a constant patrol had to be kept in 'home' waters in case it decided to venture out. Nevertheless, inactive though it was, the Grand Fleet fulfilled all the Admiralty's 'ultimate objectives', the required principles of sea power, a perfect example of Mahan's 'silent pressure'.

The most tragic example of the fallibility of the battle-cruisers is the story of HMS *Hood*, the 'Mighty Hood', which went up against the *Bismarck* in May 1941. Apparently learning from the fate of the British battle-cruisers at Jutland (although the Director of Naval Construction wisely regarded her design as suspect, going as far as to suggest that she be scrapped on the stocks), the *Hood's* armour was strengthened, adding a further 5,000 tons (5,100 tonnes) to her displacement and thereby reducing her speed by 2 knots. She was, however, one of the most graceful and elegant capital ships ever built, the pride of the Royal Navy and the darling of foreign ports in which she showed the flag. For instance, the Mayor of San Francisco expressed the international fondness felt for the *Hood* when she visited the city, when he said, 'We surrender our city to you. We capitulate.'

A U.S. Navy recruiting poster of the 1930s.

HMS *Inflexible* – 1908	
Displacement	17,250 tons (17.530 tonnes)
Length	530 ft (160 m)
Armament	8 12-in
	16 4-in
	3 4-in AA
	5 18-in torpedo tubes
	7 machine guns
Armour	6-in (15-cm) steel belt
	7-in (18-cm) turrets
	10-in (25-cm) conning tower
	2.0 to 0.75-in (5.1 to 1.9-cm) decks
Speed	25 knots and above

HMS *Lion* – 1912	
Displacement	29,680 tons (30,155 tonnes)
Length	660 ft (200 m)
Armament	8 13.5-in
	16 4-in
	1 4-in AA
	2 21-in torpedo tubes
Armour	4 to 9-in (10 to 23-cm) belt
	4 to 9-in (10 to 23-cm) turrets
	2.5 to 1-in (6.4 to 2.5-cm) decks
Speed	27 knots

HMS *Hood* – 1920	
Displacement	41,200 tons (41,860 tonnes)
Length	860 ft (262 m)
Armament	8 15-in
	14 4-in
	24 2-pounders
	20 machine guns
	5 UP batteries
	4 21-in torpedo tubes
Armour	12-in (30.5-cm) belt
	15-in (38-cm) turrets – front
	up to 3-in (8-cm) decks
Speed	28.5 knots

ASSURANCE

For Young Men

**Good Health · Travel · Steady
Pay · Educational Courses
and Recreation are assured
the Enlisted Personnel – –**

Of the NAVY

It was proposed that the *Hood* would undergo complete reconstruction in 1939, providing her with new, more powerful engines, and strengthening both her vertical and deck armour, thus increasing her 'zone of immunity'. This would cause her to be out of commission for at least two years, and when, towards the end of the 1930s, war clouds began to gather, the reconstruction was cancelled and the *Hood* went into action against the *Bismarck* mounting her original armour. After six minutes – during which 93 15-in shells were fired by the German battleship – plunging fire at 18,000 yd (16,500 m) penetrated *Hood*'s armour detonating the 100 tons (102 tonnes) of high explosive stored in her after-turret ammunition locker. The *Hood* became one huge fireball, split in two and sank, taking down with her 1,416 of her crew of 1,419.

At the end of the First World War the Allied maritime nations sat back and took stock of their shipping losses, which were appalling. Great Britain alone had all but been brought to her knees by the German U-Boat campaign. She had lost 2,408 merchant ships, a total of 7,760,000 gross tons (7,884,000 tonnes), which, even taking into account a feverish wartime replacement of shipping, still amounted to a loss of over 3,000,000 gross tons. (3,048,000 tonnes). This represented only 16 per cent of her prewar tonnage, which at the time accounted for nearly half the world's merchant shipping.

The Interwar Years

On paper the Royal Navy was still the most powerful fleet; its nearest rival, Germany, had scuttled most of its ships at Scapa Flow in 1919. But a paper fleet it was: under-armoured battle-cruisers had demonstrated their vulnerability; a third of Britain's battleships carried 12-in guns; and only the *Hood*, a doubtful battle-cruiser, was under construction. On the other hand, the United States Navy, which made no secret of its bid to become the world's principle naval power, had begun an extensive war-ship-building programme – six 43,000-ton (43,700-tonne) battleships carrying 12 16-in guns and six 43,000-ton (73,700-tonne) battle-cruisers carrying eight 16-in guns. Not to be outdone, the Japanese, only too aware of America's ambitions in the Pacific, followed suit with their '8 – 8 programme'. Japan proposed to build eight

16-in-gunned battleships and eight similarly armed battle-cruisers.

In order to avoid a postwar recession and compensate for the expanded economy brought about by wartime production, the United States looked to the Pacific to augment its world trade. The Japanese Empire, nettled by a proposed American naval base at Cavite in the Philippines – in Japanese eyes another Port Arthur – had its own plans for the area. To become and remain a first-class world power dominating the Far East, Japan needed access to oil, coal, tin, rice, iron ore and a host of other vital raw materials, all lying on her doorstep but controlled by Western Imperialist nations. Japan sat back to await her opportunity which eventually presented itself in 1941 after the outbreak of the Second World War.

Meanwhile, startled into action, Great Britain set in motion a programme for four 48,500-ton (49,300-tonne) battle-cruisers – G.3s armed with nine 16-in guns and having a speed of 32 knots – to be followed by an unspecified number (four or five) of 43,000-ton (43,700-tonne) battleships mounting nine 18-in guns capable of delivering a 3,200-lb (1,450-kg) shell up to 30,000 yd (27,000 m). It was time for the navies of the world to pause and think about the implications.

Despite the growing influence of the 'Big-Navy' lobby in Washington, which sought to provide the United States with a navy capable of successfully engaging the combined fleets of Great Britain and Japan, Congress decided to call a halt to the arms race. President Harding invited the other maritime nations – Great Britain, Japan, France and Italy – to a conference in Washington on the limitation of naval armament. The Washington Conference opened on 21 November 1931, and after much spirited and often bitter wrangling, the Treaty for the Limitation of Armament was signed in February 1922. As a result, the battle fleet of Great Britain was limited to 22 ships (580,450 tons/589,740 tonnes); Britain was forced to scrap 18 existing ships and four new ones, but allowed to complete the *Nelson* and *Rodney*. The United States was to scrap 16 battleships, retaining 18 (500,650 tons/508,660 tonnes), and, to its bitter disappointment, Japan was only allowed to retain ten capital ships (301,320 tons/306,140 tonnes).

The wave of bitterness towards the Western powers which swept Japan following the Washington Conference reached a head eight years later with the signing of another agreement to extend the 'battleship holiday' to 1936. In protest at what he considered to be Japan's abject surrender to Great Britain and the United States, a young naval officer, Lieutenant Kusukara, committed hari-kiri, kneeling in the sleeping berth of a train, and Admiral Takarabe, chief Japanese delegate at the Conference, was presented with a dagger with which to commit suicide. Further ritual suicides and political assassinations led to an emotional frenzy which finally brought down the government. Japan withdrew from the League of Nations, seized Manchuria and began to plan for the likelihood of a war against the United States, Great Britain and, if necessary, the Soviet Union. An astonished Western world was given a glimpse of the national frenzy that was later to drive Japan's young soldiers, sailors and airmen to undertake kamikaze missions, almost with joy.

France and Italy were, to be in line with Japan, each limited to ten battleships, 221,170 tons (224,710 tonnes) and 182,800 tons (185,725 tonnes) respectively. The size of battleships was limited to a displacement of 35,000 tons (35,560 tonnes), mounting guns to a maximum calibre of 16 in. The Washington Treaty clearly appeared to endorse the contention of the more conservative naval planners, that the big gun was still the dominant weapon at sea. The lessons and statistics of the First World War were disregarded – far, far more ships had been sent to the bottom by torpedo and mine than the big gun – and the growing threat from naval aircraft was ignored completely. Unwittingly, however, the delegates at the Conference had sealed the fate of the capital ship by allowing a number of battleship hulls already on the stocks to be converted into aircraft carriers.

Almost overnight there was an astonishing increase in the weight and size of aircraft carriers. The two American CVs, the *Lexington* and *Saratoga*, commissioned in 1927, had a length of 890 feet, displaced over 33,000 tons and had a speed of 33 knots, housing between 70 and 80 aircraft. Japan immediately began to rebuild two of her proposed battle-cruisers as equally large aircraft carriers.

Led by the Conte di Cavour, *the Italian Fleet steams line ahead during the 1938 Naval Review. The battleship* Giulio Cesare *and a heavy cruiser are astern of the* Cavour.

The German battleship
Admiral Graf Spee steams
to take up station as a
commerce raider in August
1939, a month before the
Second World War broke
out.

Germany, who had not been invited to the Washington Conference, became the cause of a second naval arms race which erupted during the mid-1930s. Following defeat in 1918, Germany had been restricted by the Treaty of Versailles to a fleet of six pre-dreadnoughts to act as coastal defence ships, the replacement for any of which was not to exceed 10,000 tons (10,200 tonnes); Germany was totally barred from building submarines. The German naval architects overcame the weight problem in a startlingly novel way, much to the consternation of the other European navies, especially that of France. The *Deutschland*, the first of the 'Panzerschiff' – armoured ship – laid down in 1929, was obviously intended as a commerce raider. With an undeclared displacement of nearly 12,000 tons (12,200 tonnes) (17 per cent above the limit) and mounting six 11-in guns, with a secondary armament of eight 5-in and six 4.1-in guns, she was powered by diesel engines which gave her a maximum speed of 28 knots and allowed her a cruising range of 10,000 nautical miles (18,520 km) at 20 knots. Although greeted with hysterical joy by the German people and with considerable apprehension by the rest of the world, the *Deutschland* (later renamed *Lützow*) and her two sister ships, *Admiral Graf Spee* and *Admiral Scheer*, proved to be more of a propaganda coup than a serious threat as warships. The pocket-battleships, as they were soon dubbed, were, in practice, a failure. Over-gunned for the role of commerce raider and with insufficient speed to catch a heavy cruiser, they had neither firepower nor armour to engage a capital ship, and their maximum speed of 28.5 knots made it difficult for them to escape the most modern battleships. Nevertheless, their grossly exaggerated performance – the Nazi propaganda machine soon slipped into gear after 1933 – whipped up a fervour of national pride in Germany at what they believed to be the rebirth of their once proud navy, and disturbed the rest of Europe. Worse was to follow.

The Admiral Graf Spee, only slightly damaged, off Montevideo, Uruguay, after her action with three British cruisers.

Adolf Hitler, repudiating the Versailles Treaty, laid down two fast battle-cruisers, the *Scharnhorst* and the *Gneisenau* in 1934, with a declared displacement of 26,000 tons (26,400 tonnes), which ultimately came out to be 32,000 tons (32,500 tonnes). Underdeclaration of weight, begun in the late 1920s, became a deliberate policy after the National Socialist Government came into power. Throwing caution to the winds, relying correctly on the vacillation of the other European powers, Hitler announced the construction of two further 31-knot battleships, the *Bismarck* and the *Tirpitz*, and a number of heavy cruisers. The battleships were 'intended' to meet the maximum tonnage agreed worldwide of 35,000 tons (35,560 tonnes) and the heavy cruisers of 10,000 tons (10,200 tonnes) – they emerged with a displacement of 42,000 tons (42,700 tonnes) and 15,000 tons (15,240 tonnes) respectively, part of what the Germans termed their 'Z Plan'; they were also secretly building U-Boats. 'Plan Z', finalized between 1937 and 1938, called for a fleet capable of crippling the mercantile marine of Great Britain and France in the event of a war with those two countries.

Plan Z

6 battleships in commission by 1944
8 armoured cruisers: 4 by 1943 and the rest by 1948
4 aircraft carriers: 2 by 1941 and the other by 1947
223 U-Boats: 128 by 1943 and a further 95 by 1947

These dates, projected by the German Kriegsmarine, were to be turned upside down by Hitler's impatience.

France, disturbed by the advent of the German pocket-battleship, rapidly built two 25,000-ton (25,400-tonne) 13-in gunned battle-cruisers, the *Strasbourg* and the *Dunkerque*. Italy replied with a series of fast graceful 35,000-ton (35,560-tonne) battleships. A Franco-Italian naval arms race was on for the control of the Mediterranean. Naval arms treaties became meaningless. The supposed 35,000-ton (35,560-tonne) Italian *Littorio* and sister ship, the *Vittorio Veneto*, both launched in 1937, actually displaced over 41,000 tons (41,660 tonnes) when they were commissioned, 6,000 tons (6,100 tonnes) over the

The French battleship Richelieu *takes heavy seas across her bows while on route to the Pacific, as part of a British Fleet in 1944.*

An artist's impression of the 63,000-ton (64,000-tonne) 'Montana' class battleship. This class was intended to be the largest United States battleship, but it was never built.

treaty limits, an increase of 18 per cent, a discrepancy that no competent naval architect could incur by accident. Mounting 15-in guns and carrying 14-in (36-cm) thick belt armour, they still had an average trial speed of 31 knots but, in practice, this never exceeded 28 knots. When two more of these hard-hitting ships, the *Impero* and the *Roma*, were laid down in 1938, and four older battleships brilliantly reconstructed to modern standards, it became obvious that Italian dictator Benito Mussolini was challenging the Royal Navy's supremacy of the Mediterranean and at-tempting to make good his boast of *Mare Nostrum*.

As early as 1934 the Admiralty had advised the Government that the Royal Navy was under-strength in the likely event of war against Germany or Japan, or possibly both, before 1941, and urged that new battleships should be laid down as soon as the current naval treaty expired. A capital-ship programme was sanctioned following the 1935 Three-Power Treaty between Great Britain, the United States and France. Five 44,000-ton (44,700-tonne) 14-in gunned battleships were ordered.

The maximum calibre for guns was limited to 14 in by the Conference, but both France and Italy had by then secretly committed themselves to 15 in, and the United States had insisted on a clause allowing her 16-in guns if Japan failed to conform. Thus Great Britain ended up the only country to arm her capital ships with 14-in guns. It was hoped all ships would be in commission by 1941; in fact the last two did not join the Fleet until 1942, three years after the outbreak of war.

When Hitler and Mussolini signed a military alliance in 1936 forming the Rome-Berlin Axis, there appeared the strong likelihood that the Royal Navy would also have the Italian Fleet to contend with if war broke out, presenting a severe challenge to her mastery of the sea. Already Hitler's armies occupied the Rhineland, Italy had attacked Abyssinia and in the Far East Japan had invaded Manchuria and then the Chinese mainland. Axis troops, especially those in the fledgling Luftwaffe, were also gaining invaluable wartime experience fighting alongside Franco's nationalists in the Spanish Civil War.

A German propaganda painting of a German pocket-battleship.

The Second World War

Even so, Hitler's invasion of Poland, precipitating the Second World War, caught both the Royal Navy and the German *Kriegsmarine* unprepared. Great Britain's 15 elderly capital ships, several of which were doubtful battle-cruisers (battle-cruisers of the late 1930s, such as those of Germany, France and other fleets, were almost as heavily armoured as conventional battleships), were unlikely to be a match for the fast German and Italian capital ships, particularly when the super-battleships *Bismarck* and *Tirpitz* came into commission. The first of Britain's own up-to-date capital ships was unlikely to be ready before the end of 1940.

In the Far East the Imperial Japanese Navy had clamoured for an extensive

reconstruction and shipbuilding programme to enable it to compete with the capital-ship strength of Great Britain and the United States. Giving two years' notice of her withdrawal from the 1930 Naval Treaty, Japan nonetheless gave an undertaking to abide by the spirit of the 1936 Treaty, while reserving the right to build battleships of up to 44,000 tons (44,700 tonnes) displacement. As it became clear that the Imperial dockyards would never be able to compete with those of Great Britain and the U.S.A., Japanese admirals persuaded their government to disregard the treaty restrictions. They called for battleships large enough to out-gun anything the Americans could send into the Pacific which was governed by the size of ship that could pass through the Panama Canal, about 60,000 tons (61,000 tonnes).

Right: One of the two largest battleships ever to go into commission, the Yamato is fitted out at Kune, Japan in 1941.

Below: The 72,000-ton (73,000-tonne) Yamato during her running trials on 30 October 1941. Her sister ship, the Musashi, displaced the same weight, and was sunk by aircraft in 1944.

This saw the birth of the monstrous 'Yamato' class. Four of these 72,000-ton (73,150-tonne) ships were laid down, but the *Musashi* was the only other one to be completed as a battleship. When they came into commission, in 1941 and 1942 respectively, the biggest capital ships ever built, they were already an anachronism, ironically enough made obsolete by the very tactics demonstrated by Japanese naval flyers. At the time, however, they were considered the ultimate in naval power and might. Apart from displacing 72,000 tons (73,150 tonnes) full load, they mounted nine 18-in guns, each weighing 157 tons (160 tonnes) and capable of delivering 3,220 lb (1,460 kg) a maximum range of over 25.5 miles (41.0 km), and 12 6-in guns as secondary armament. The forest of anti-aircraft guns comprised six 5-in AA, 147 25 mm AA and four 12.7 mm AA. The heaviest belt armour was 15.75 in (40 cm) thick, the deck armour to 8 in (18–20 cm) and the main turrets 19.75 to 25.5 in (50.17-64.77 cm). Yet despite this massive armour, they could reach an amazing maximum speed of 27.5 knots, powered by four-shaft steam turbines generating a very impressive 150,000 shp.

The British battleship HMS Duke of York *in a choppy sea.*

E. TUFNELL.

At the beginning of the Second World War, the battleship was still regarded as the mainstay of naval power and it was not until Italy entered the war that this concept was thrown into doubt. From their inception, German capital ships were seen as commerce raiders for at no time did the *Kriegsmarine* seriously contemplate facing the Royal Navy in another Jutland. But the Mediterranean theatre could prove to be quite different. When Mussolini plunged Italy into the war on the side of Germany in June 1940, the Italian Navy boasted six battleships, including the newly completed 41,000-ton (41,700-tonne) 15-in gunned *Littorio* and *Vittorio Veneto*. Ranged against these were the ageing *Barham*, *Warspite*, *Queen Elizabeth* and *Valiant*. On paper the odds were heavily stacked in favour of the Italian Fleet should it ever bring the British Mediterranean Fleet to a pitched battle. These odds were dramatically levelled on

the night of 10 November, 1940 when 21 Swordfish torpedo bombers from the aircraft carrier *Illustrious* put half the Italian battle fleet out of action as it lay in harbour. With only 11 18-in aerial torpedo hits, they sank the *Conte di Cavour* and badly damaged the *Littorio* and the *Caio Duilio*.

The more conservative naval planners, champions of the battleship, were horrified; the advocates of naval air power, until now in the shade, jubilant. In London Commander Minoru Genda, the Japanese naval attaché and himself an airman, closely followed the Fleet Air Arm attack at Taranto. A full report found its way to Admiral Isoruku Yamamoto, Commander-in-Chief of the Imperial Fleet, who was also a pilot and a staunch advocate of air power – the attack at Taranto triggered off a very courageous plan in his mind to free the Pacific of an American presence.

Heavy American guns open up at Guam in 1944. The American Navy has continued to make use of the battleship to dominate an enemy shoreline or rear area. The USS New Jersey was used to hit targets many miles inland in support of the Marines serving in the Lebanon.

THE RISE OF NAVAL AIR POWER

A Royal Navy short seaplane taxies to her carrier before the raid on the Zeppelin sheds at Cuxhaven in 1914.

Ironically Admiral Sir John 'Jackie' Fisher was one of the first fleet admirals to see the flimsy, new-fangled flying machine as a lethal attack weapon. He and Admiral Scott, although probably the most fervent champions of the 'big gun', were both totally convinced that the navies of the future would become airborne, making the battleship obsolete as the *Dreadnought* had made all other capital ships of the time obsolete. Such prophecies, smacking of Jules Verne, were all too heady for most serving officers and naval planners, especially when based on an 852-ft (260-m) 'hop' by the Wright Brothers in their rickety 'heavier-than-air' machine, and a few subsequent flights by other pioneer aviators. Admittedly Louis Blériot had

flown the English Channel from Calais to Dover, but as the critics of flying were quick to point out, he would never have made it had not a providential shower cooled down his overheating 25-hp Anzani engine. The naval aeroplane critics were not being wholly reactionary: fast and heavily armoured, the *Dreadnought* with her big, efficient guns was already a proven factor. The critics simply could not see that these flimsy, unreliable aeroplanes could possibly offer any sort of threat to her. The more thoughtful ones, and there were many, could, however, see a valuable reconnaissance role for naval aircraft.

During the intervening years between Wright's Kitty Hawk flight and the outbreak of the First World War, the aeroplane developed at an alarming rate, and more and more people became convinced of its potential as a military weapon. In naval circles it was welcomed as a further reconnaissance arm, one which, coupled

with Marconi's recently invented 'wireless', would allow them for the first time to probe quickly beyond the horizon. At first, fleet commanders were reluctant to be saddled with seaplane carriers which were converted merchantmen, which slowed down the warships, making them vulnerable to submarine attack. Later it was the futility of flying aircraft on and off a battle-cruiser which, admittedly, had been converted too quickly; practically every landing ended in disaster. Nevertheless, the strong lobby of naval-air-arm enthusiasts pressured the Admiralty to continue its support for naval air power and, by the end of hostilities, the Royal Navy led the field in the development of the aircraft carrier, but had no clear idea how to exploit its obvious potential.

The First World War

One fundamental principle, however, was established during the course of the First World War, a principle that represented one of the most significant developments in naval warfare: the attempt to mount an attack on an enemy beyond the horizon. Once this principle had been established it was eagerly seized upon by naval airmen, particularly those of the United States and Japan. The first attempt to project firepower beyond the horizon took place on Christmas Day 1914. The raid on the Zeppelin sheds at Cuxhaven was, in itself, a total failure, but the lessons learned from it caused the champions of naval air power to examine carrier-borne aircraft more closely, laying the foundations for the mass naval aerial attacks of the Second World War.

The air strike on Cuxhaven at the mouth of the River Elbe was a diversion planned to draw out heavy units of the High Seas Fleet at Wilhelmshaven into a submarine trap. In perfect conditions, sunny weather with a flat calm sea, the three seaplane carriers, *Empress*, *Engadine* and *Riviera*, escorted by the Harwich Force, destroyers and light cruisers, sailed deep into the Heligoland Bight and lay to for action. Nine seaplanes, Short Folders and Types 74 and 135, were to be used in the attack, carrying bombloads, which, even had the raid been successful, would have caused only minor damage to the Zeppelin sheds. In the event, two of the seaplanes, cranked over the sides, failed to take off

Eugene Ely's Curtiss Hudson takes off from the cruiser USS Pennsylvania after he had become the first man to land an aircraft on a ship.

because of engine trouble. The remaining seven ran into dense coastal fog, raised by the warm sun, were unable to locate their target, and were forced to jettison their bombs. On their return they had been instructed to fly over the Schillig Roads and observe the German Fleet units. The unprecedented sight of Royal Navy Air Service (R.N.A.S.) aircraft circling above their base threw some German commanders into a panic, and a number of minor collisions occurred as they weighed anchor to scatter. Of the strike force, only two located their parent ship to be cranked inboard. The remaining five, running out of fuel, were forced to 'ditch' and their crews were picked up by various ships. By now the German Navy had been alerted and a flight of Zeppelins bombed the returning Allied naval force which was dashing for Harwich, but did not inflict any damage.

The result of this abortive air strike was to harden the opposition of reactionary fleet commanders towards seaplanes and their carriers, and cause R.N.A.S. aviators to clamour for a more reliable way to get naval aircraft airborne. By the end of the First World War, after numerous schemes

had been tried, often more imaginative than practical, the aircraft carrier was established as the only practical method of operating aircraft at sea.

Strangely enough, the Americans, who had led the way in deck landing, putting a Curtiss D IV Military down on the deck of the cruiser USS *Pennsylvania* in 1911, showed little interest in naval aviation. It was left to the Japanese to be the first to put a purpose-built carrier into commission. More than any other nation, Japan, whose interests lay in the vastness of the Pacific, was aware of the importance of carrier-borne aircraft, and much of her future naval strategy was to revolve round the aircraft carrier.

One American who clearly foresaw the use of naval aircraft as an attack weapon was Brigadier-General 'Billy' Mitchell of the U.S. Army Air Force. He forcefully maintained – his lack of technical and political judgement led him into charges of gross insubordination towards his superiors which resulted in a courtmartial – that aircraft could sink any surface ship, and battleships were therefore obsolete. A fanatical advocate of air power, he brought the worst out in the naval authorities who were equally fanatically wedded to the big-gun battleship. Without regard to future development they maintained that existing naval aircraft could not sink a battleship with bombs. 'Billy' Mitchell was, in hindsight, of course proved right and naval bombing and torpedo attack eventually were accepted by all navies.

Mitchell did win permission to carry out bombing trials against surrendered German warships off the Virginia Capes in 1921. Armed with small and not very powerful bombs, his aircraft attacked the anchored ships under ideal conditions and, in short order, sank a U-Boat and a destroyer. The older light cruiser *Frankfurt* proved more difficult to sink, but it was the battleship *Ostfriesland* that gave his pilots the most trouble. Ordered to pause between bombing sorties to allow naval observers to go aboard to assess the damage resulting from each attack, Mitchell completely ignored the rules and instructed his pilots to keep up a continuous attack. When after two days' bombing the *Ostfriesland* did finally go down, the sinking sparked off acrimonious exchanges between Mitchell and his detractors. In a narrow sense his critics were right; all that had been achieved was the eventual sinking of a battleship from the air, while it was stationary and unable to defend itself. What they failed to grasp was Mitchell's vision of the future, that aircraft would become faster and more reliable and that bombs and torpedoes would become more powerful. Entrenched naval opinion won this first round. Even naval officers with an open mind who steered a middle course were reluctant to abandon the big-gun battleship, a proven weapon, in favour of a weapon of unproven worth. So the

roles of carrier were considered to be threefold: to protect the battleship against enemy aerial attack; to scout for the fleet and spot for its guns; and to slow down a fleeing enemy squadron to allow the battle line to catch up. This happened at Matapan in 1941, when Albacore torpedo bombers from *Formidable* slowed down an Italian fleet, which resulted in the sinking of three cruisers and two destroyers. It was also a Fleet Air Arm (F.A.A.) Swordfish that crippled the *Bismarck*, allowing *King George V* and *Rodney* to catch up and engage her. The concept of using aircraft carriers as an attacking strike force to carry the battle beyond the visual range had hardly been considered, but the air arm of the Imperial Japanese Navy was soon to turn its attention in that direction.

After the First World War carrier construction and development had gone along at a leisurely pace; the *Eagle*, for instance, began her trials in 1920, but was not fully completed and operational until four years later. Following the Washington Conference, Great Britain and the United States found themselves with 135,000 tons (137,000 tonnes) for conversion to carriers, Japan with 81,000 tons (82,300 tonnes) and both France and Italy with 60,000 tons (61,000 tonnes). Overnight the size of carriers escalated from 22,000 tons (22,350 tonnes) to 33,000 tons (33,530 tonnes), able to house over 80 aircraft in below-deck hangars. Besotted as it was by the big-gun capital ship, the Conference was blind to the implications of the 'scrap or convert' clause in the treaty; by encouraging the building of large carriers, it was sealing the fate of the battleship.

It took 'Billy' Mitchell's naval aircraft two days to sink the old German battleship Ostfriesland.

NAVAL AIRCRAFT

During the formative years of the carrier following the First World War, the aircraft in use were ones that had already seen service in that war. Slow, with speeds hovering around 100 mph (160 km/h), but highly manoeuvrable and with low landing speeds, they were ideal aircraft with which to experiment in deck-landing techniques and tactics. They had little value as strike weapons for their main armament consisted of only .303 calibre machine guns mounted on the cowling and another on a flexible mounting in the rear cockpit and the bombs carried were small, hardly powerful enough to do any real damage. The torpedo bomber offered the greatest potential, although the torpedo itself was not completely reliable, even by the early stages of the Second World War, and it was not easy to deliver. The optimum height for 'dropping' was 50 ft (15 m), above that it was liable to break its back; below that it would skid along the surface. At times the delicate mechanism which guided the torpedo could be damaged on impact, causing it to veer off course or to sink harmlessly to the bottom. Other times the 'exploders' fitted to the nose would fail to detonate the warhead.

The Golden Age of flying, the late 1920s and early 1930s, when records were being smashed one after the other and countries were taking a marked interest in air races, saw a rapid development in the aircraft themselves. Great attention was paid to the overall design and construction of airframes; improved engines were pushed to their limit by new fuels and lubricants; retractable undercarriages were introduced which drew up the landing gear into the fuselage, cutting down wind resistance and increasing speed. Speeds increased dramatically: the 1925 Curtiss F6C had a speed of 159 mph (256 km/h); the 1936 Grumman F3F-1 had a maximum speed of

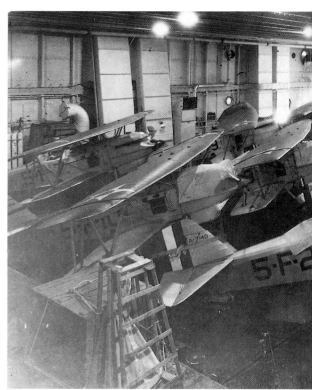

231 mph (372 km/h); and when war broke out in 1939, the Japanese Mitsubishi A6M2 'Zero' carrier-borne plane was capable of reaching a speed of 331 mph (533 km/h). The performance of Fleet Air Arm aircraft sadly lagged behind those of the United States and Japan, particularly the bomber/torpedo aircraft. Whereas the Japanese Nakajima B6N2 Tenzan 'Heavenly Mountain', dubbed 'Jill' by the Allies, had a speed of 199 mph (320 km/h), and the U.S. Douglas TBD-1 Devastator had achieved 225 mph (362 km/h), the F.A.A. had the Fairey Swordfish, the antiquated 'Stringbag', with a top speed of 139 mph (224 km/h) and the Fairey Albacore with one of 161 mph (259 km/h). Yet, despite their lack of speed, these British torpedo bombers were among the most successful throughout the Second World War.

As the war progressed, naval aircraft such as the American Vought Corsair reached a top speed of 415 mph (668 km/h). After the war speeds continued to climb, but there is a limit to the speed at which a propeller-driven aircraft can fly; as the spinning tips approach the speed of sound, this sets up violent air currents or 'turbulence' which causes the aircraft to vibrate and increases the air resistance. Since before the war, aircraft designers had been working on a propulsion unit that dispensed with propellers. The introduction of jet-propelled aircraft became the greatest step forward since flying itself, and once the sound barrier had been broken [about 760 mph (1,223 km/h) at sea level, 660 mph (1,062 km/h) at 36,000 ft (11,000 m)] speeds began to be measured in units of the speed of sound – 'Mach'.

The seaborne use of such high-speed aircraft raised a number of problems in carrier design, but most of the fastest aircraft have been adapted, despite increased weights and landing speeds.

Far left top: A flight of US Navy Douglas SBD Dauntless bombers in 1944.

Far left centre: A Marine ordnanceman services a Vought F4U, on board USS Block Island in June 1945.

Far left bottom: The old and the new: a Grumman F6F Hellcat flies in formation with the modern fighter, the Grumman F14 Tomcat.

Left: A flight of British Aerospace Sea Harriers. The Harrier proved itself during the Falklands War.

Below left: Curtiss F6C-3 fighters, stacked in the hangar of USS Lexington in 1928.

RELATIVE SPEEDS OF NAVAL AIRCRAFT

Aircraft Designation/ Name	Country of Origin	Date	Ceiling		Speed	
			feet	metres	mph	km/h
Short 184	Great Britain	1915	9,000	2,700	90	145
Sopwith Camel	Great Britain	1917	17,000	5,200	125	200
Boeing F4B	U.S.A.	1929	27,000	8,200	180	290
Aichi 'Val'	Japan	1940	32,000	9,750	250	400
Mitsubishi A6M5 'Zero'	Japan	1941	35,000	10,700	350	560
Vought Corsair F4U	U.S.A.	1943	34,000	10,400	415	670
Hawker Sea Hawk	Great Britain	1953	44,000	13,400	560	900
Douglas Skyray	U.S.A.	1956	55,000	16,800	750	1,210
LTV Crusader	U.S.A.	1956	58,000	17,700	1,120	1,800
Grumman F-14 Tomcat	U.S.A.	1974	56,000	17,100	1,564	2,516
McDonnell-Douglas Phantom	U.S.A.	1960	70,000	21,300	1,905	3,070
Hawker-Siddeley Harrier (V/STOL)	Great Britain	1971	50,000	15,200	740	1,190

Carriers at War

A flight of Fairey Swordfish torpedo bombers flies above HMS Ark Royal in 1939.

At the outset of the Second World War, which began as a European conflict, only Great Britain among the belligerents had a sizeable carrier fleet, but one that was neither well-organized nor well-supplied. The amalgamation of the R.N.A.S. with the Royal Flying Corps in 1918 to form the Royal Air Force saw the Royal Navy lose control of its air arm, to become the poor relation in the scramble for available aircraft. By the time it won back control, in 1937, it was almost too late. Already the Americans had six times the number of naval aircraft and Japan three times the number, but even more alarming was the fact that their aircraft were infinitely superior to those of the Fleet Air Arm (F.A.A.). Britain still clung to archaic biplanes for torpedo bombing and had no modern fighters at all until the Spitfire and Hurricane were adapted for naval duties.

The six frontline carriers of the Royal Navy were among the best in the world, but the Admiralty failed completely to grasp the implication of their potential as an offensive force. The British were still wedded to the notion that the roles of naval aircraft were reconnaissance, convoy protection, defence of a fleet and slowing down heavy enemy units to allow the main fleet to close and engage. By splitting them up between the Western Approaches and Scapa Flow, with *Glorious* in the Mediterranean and *Eagle* in the Far East, a potential 250-strong offensive weapon was instead deployed in small defensive units. It was not until Japan attacked Pearl Harbor that the full potential of a carrier group as a mobile strike force was fully appreciated. Mistakenly, the Royal Navy at first employed its fleet carriers on anti-submarine patrol and on searching for German surface raiders that had taken up station before the war started. Their vulnerability when performing this task was brutally exposed when, after just two weeks of war, *U.29* sent *Courageous* to the bottom. Following the Norwegian campaign during which *Glorious* was sunk by the *Scharnhorst* and *Gneisenau* while ferrying fighter planes back to Britain, the Royal Navy sent most of its carriers into the Mediterranean to deal with the added threat of the Italian fleet.

There, the F.A.A. carried out one of its most successful raids. Just after dusk on 11 November 1940, 21 Swordfish were flown off *Illustrious*, 11 armed with torpedoes, six with bombs, and the other four with flares. They headed for the naval base at Taranto, 170 miles (270 km) away, where the main units of the Italian fleet – six battleships and six heavy cruisers – lay complacently in harbour, heavily protected by submarine nets and barrage balloons. Easily avoiding the latter, the slow lumbering Swordfish formed up into two waves for a low-level attack. Lit up by descending flares, the shocked Italian gunners scarcely had time to man their stations before the aerial torpedoes were crashing into their battleships; at that stage of the war the Italians had no radar to detect incoming aircraft. With just 11 torpedoes the *Illustrious* strike force had put half the Italian battle fleet out of action, as well as destroying a seaplane base and damaging the oil depot. The *Conte di Cavour* would never sail again, and the *Littorio* and *Caio Duilio* would be out of service for months. This F.A.A. victory was to have far-reaching repercussions, far beyond the results of the raid for it demonstrated in no uncertain manner that carrier-borne aircraft could be used as a devastating strike force. That a mere 21 outdated aircraft could wreak such havoc among a fleet of modern battleships in a matter of a few minutes did not go unnoticed in the Far East. This F.A.A. success crystallized a bold (later to be proved foolhardy) plan in the mind of Admiral Yamamoto, the most influential supporter of naval air power in the Imperial Japanese Navy.

HMS Eagle (*ex-battleship Almirante Cochrane*) *shows her distinctive battleship lines and elongated island. She carried 21 aircraft and was launched in 1918.*

The architect of the Japanese raid on Pearl Harbor, Admiral Yamamoto.

A Sea Hurricane waits to be
launched from a CAM-ship
(Catapult Aircraft Merchant
ship). The Hurricane had to
ditch in the sea after its fuel
ran out.

A typical example of a
MAC-ship (Merchant
Aircraft Carrier), Empire
MacAndrew. These ships
were fitted with a simple
flight-deck and could operate
four aircraft.

THE ESCORT CARRIER

The tactics of the *Kriegsmarine* in the Second World War were simple and direct: to stop the vital flow of imported raw materials and, later, Lease Lend goods and thus destroy Allied commerce. When surface raiding proved unsuccessful, the whole campaign was altered to revolve about the U-Boat fleet which attacked either singly or in wolf-packs. Once most of Europe capitulated, Admiral Dönitz was able to deploy his U-Boat flotillas from the North Cape to Biscay, allowing giant four-engined Fw 200 Kondor reconnaissance bombers to range deep into the 'Black Gap' in mid-Atlantic, out of range of Allied shore-based air patrols.

To counter bombing from these aircraft and stop them shadowing convoys to radio information to the wolf-packs, it was thought acceptable to lose a fighter aircraft if it could destroy a Kondor. Thus a number of merchantmen had a catapult fitted to the forecastle to enable the ship to launch a single Hawker Hurricane fighter. These were designated CAM-ships (Catapult-Armed Merchant ships). It was a hazardous, one-way trip for the pilots, who had to bale out after making their kill, hoping to be picked up by a convoy escort – there were no means of recovering aircraft after they ran out of fuel.

Successes were marginal until the MAC-ship (Merchant Aircraft Carrier – a merchant ship fitted with a flight-deck, but which still carried cargo and was manned by a civilian crew) was introduced as a stop-gap before the escort carrier, the CVE, could be produced. Nicknamed 'Banana Boats' – the first CVE, the *Audacity,* was converted from a captured German banana ship – or 'Woolworth Carriers', these escort carriers were an immediate success in convoy work, and the decline in U-Boat successes dates from their introduction. The *Audacity* carried six Martlett II (Wildcat) fighters ranged on her flight-deck; there had been no time to equip hangar decks or instal lifts. Accompanying three convoys she and her fighters accounted for 200 Kondors, either shot down or driven off.

Later, as the CVEs improved in quality – displacing about 9,000 tons (9,100 tonnes) and carrying a mixed complement of 30 or so aircraft, or attack squadrons of Seafires and Sea Hurricanes – they took on AS (Anti-Submarine) duties, fleet protection and gave cover for amphibious landings.

Not that it was easy to land the later 400 mph Supermarine Seafire on the comparatively short, lurching flight-deck of an escort carrier. The onus was on the batman to bring the aircraft in at exactly the correct direction, height and speed. Failure to do so often led to costly crashes. The aircraft would come hurtling in with its hook down ready to take up one of the arrester wires; failure to cut the engine at the precise moment would send it skimming across the deck to land in the heavy, hydraulic crash barriers. More often than not the aircraft would overturn leaving the pilot dangling upside down from his safety harness.

Two days later, 10 December, Japanese long-range shore-based naval bombers emphatically made the point that aircraft could deal with capital ships more effectively and economically than surface ships when the battle-cruiser *Repulse* became the first capital ship to be sunk at sea by aircraft, closely followed by her companion, the battleship *Prince of Wales*. Following so closely on the heels of the disaster at Pearl Harbor, this action signalled the end of the big-gun battleship era at sea.

A stream of brilliant successes followed for the Japanese war machine – Wake Island, the Philippines, Malaya and the Indies – in which its shore-based and carrier-borne aircraft complemented each other in the battle to gain air supremacy over Japanese objectives, prior to amphibious landings. In the course of a few short months, Japanese carriers, operating in groups, had scored a number of operational triumphs from Hawaii to Ceylon; during this time they had claimed five American battleships, two British heavy cruisers and

a light cruiser among other victims. In spite of Yamamoto's appeal for an overall strategic policy, the Japanese High Command became obsessed with acquiring oil. Singapore fell, Hong Kong surrendered, and the disastrous Battle of the Java Sea left the way open for an invasion of Ceylon or Australia. Yet still the Japanese had not achieved a decisive strategic victory that would force the United States to the negotiating table. The results of Pearl Harbor and the timely absence of the *Enterprise, Lexington* and *Saratoga* had prompted the U.S. Navy to base its future naval strategy around a rapidly growing carrier force, and the Japanese were anxious to bring about an action before the U.S. Navy became much too powerful to challenge. It was the subsequent mauling the Japanese Navy received, firstly at the Battle of the Coral Sea in May 1942 and then at Midway in the following month – battles in which it is significant that capital ships did not fire a single shot – that saw the beginning of the eclipse of the Imperial Japanese Navy.

Midway was followed by a series of hard-fought carrier battles in which both sides suffered losses, but the awesome level of production in the United States led to an overwhelming superiority in men and material that the Japanese just could not match. Japan was also suffering from a lack of trained pilots; many of Japan's most experienced airmen had been lost at Midway. This is reflected in the comparative figures for the great 'Marianas Turkey Shoot' of June 1944: for the loss of 29 American carrier-borne aircraft, the Americans shot down between 300 and 350 Japanese planes. When the Americans landed in the Philippines, the Imperial Japanese Navy flung its whole fleet into one last-ditch effort to stop them. However, the series of major naval engagements, known as the Battle of Leyte Gulf, ended in total defeat for the Japanese: they lost three battleships, including the mighty *Musashi*, four carriers, ten cruisers and nine destroyers. The sinking of the *Musashi* demonstrated once and for all that even the most powerful and well-armoured battleship ever built, which she was, could be no match for aircraft – although it did take 20 torpedoes and 17 bombs to sink her. In spite of this decisive blow to the Japanese fleet, the war in the Pacific dragged on for a further ten months, the Americans pushing back the enemy, island by island, towards the homeland. The adage that a fleet would lose ten per cent of its efficiency for every 1,000 miles (1,600 km) it steamed from its base no longer applied. The U.S. 'long-haul' Navy, 78,000 vessels in all, carried its own repair, supply and salvage vessels: among them were 104 fast oil tankers, 39 storeships, 272 cargo ships and 272 transport vessels.

It was in the course of the Philippines' operation that the Japanese introduced the most 'frightful' of all naval weapons – frightful not because of the damage they achieved, but because of the philosophical concept behind them. It was Vice-Admiral Takijiro Ohnishi who, in an attempt to ward off defeat, advocated the use of 'kamikaze' crash-dive techniques. Although the idea of a pilot committing himself in cold blood to a suicide attack was repugnant to the West, in Japan there was no shortage of young, inadequately trained pilots (they did not have to be

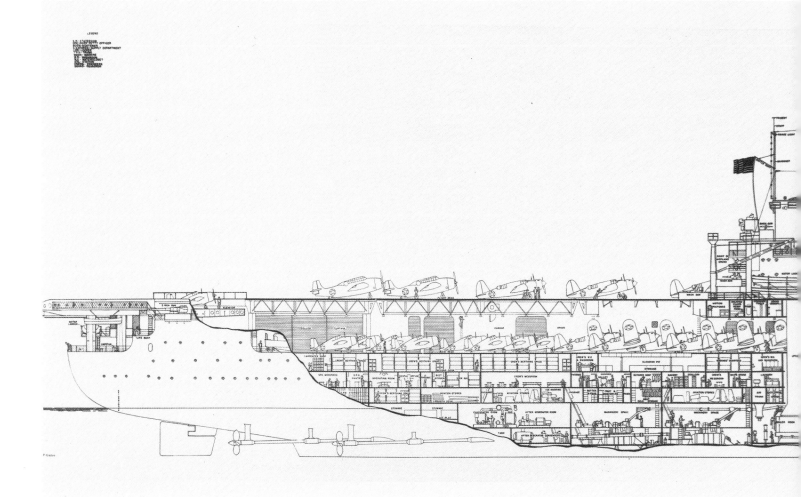

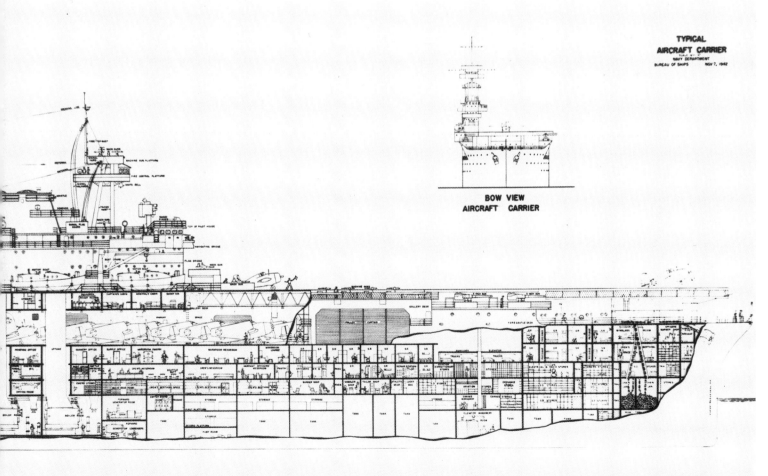

TYPICAL
AIRCRAFT CARRIER
NAVY DEPARTMENT
BUREAU OF SHIPS   NOV 7, 1942

BOW VIEW
AIRCRAFT CARRIER

taught to land) who were eager to die for the Emperor. Despite the fanaticism with which they were delivered, these 'kamikaze' attacks in no way justified the loss of brave men and aircraft – 1,228 aircraft and 298 manned bombs were expended for the loss of 34 American ships sunk and 288 damaged. By the time the Second World War ended in 1945 with the dropping of atomic bombs on Hiroshima and Nagasaki, naval air power and the carrier had proved decisive and strike aircraft had replaced the big guns of the battleship.

Postwar Carriers

At the end of the war the United States found itself with 41,000 naval aircraft deployed throughout the world and a huge carrier force; the second largest carrier fleet of 1,326 aircraft, that of Great Britain, was dwarfed by comparison. Both countries had ambitious carrier programmes in hand, and although reluctant to relinquish the superiority they had gained in naval aviation, both later curtailed these forces in the light of postwar events.

Even before peace was declared it was obvious that the ideological differences between Soviet communism and Western democracy were irreconcilable, that the gulf could only widen. The world effectively split into mutually antagonistic camps;

A Grumman TBF-6 Avenger comes into land on an 'Essex' class carrier. The Avenger had a crew of three and could carry either a 921-lb (419-kg) torpedo or 2,000 lb (910 kg) of iron bombs.

ranged on one side were the Western democracies; on the other, behind the 'Iron Curtain', were the Soviet Union and her communist satellites. Thus economically exhausted countries, instead of disarming, were forced into an arms race. To counter the possibility of Soviet aggression, the United States, Great Britain, France and other Western powers put their signatures to the North Atlantic Treaty, formed to set up a common NATO defence force. This called for a large combined fleet in which naval air power played an all-important part.

For most of the Pacific campaign, the 27,000-ton (27,400-tonne) 'Essex' class had been the mainstay of the American carrier forces, but in 1943 the 'Midways' were laid down. Capable of operating 137 aircraft, their flight-decks strengthened with 3.5-in armour, after the style of the British carriers, they had a displacement of 45,000 tons (45,700 tonnes). These 968-ft (295-m) giants were capital ships in every sense of the word, with 212,000-shp engines able to generate a speed of 33 knots. Carriers were to grow even larger as aircraft grew in size, power, range and armament. Great Britain, too, had an ambitious carrier programme, but only two were completed, the 42,000-ton (42,700-tonne) *Eagle* and *Ark Royal*; three 'Gibraltar' class fleet carriers that would have rivalled the 'Midways' in size were cancelled.

Jet Aircraft

The first jet aircraft landing was made in 1945 by a modified Vampire, touching down on *Ocean*, a Royal Navy light fleet carrier, but it was some years before jets went into active squadron service. Their coming marked another major step forward in naval air power, but it also brought with it problems for the naval architects responsible for designing carriers. The higher speeds reached by powerful jet engines – the heavy McDonnell Banshee (U.S.A.) had a speed of 600 mph (965 km/h); the lighter Supermarine Attacker (G.B.), one of 590 mph (949 km/h) – allowed wings to be reduced in size which, in turn, reduced drag. This, however, made for higher take-off and landing-on speeds which, in turn, required longer flight-decks and, as aircraft speeds continued to increase, would need progressively longer flight-decks. The answer proved to be deceptively simple –

the angled flight-deck. This ingenious idea, emanating from the Royal Aircraft Research Establishment at Farnborough, Hampshire, simultaneously solved two other problems highlighted in the Korean War of 1950. Navy jet aircraft – properly handled they had proved infinitely superior to piston-driven aircraft during this conflict – coming in fast, had only a nylon barrier between them and the forward 'deck park' of aircraft waiting to fly off, should they miss the arrester wires. This occurrence resulted in an extremely expensive waste of aircraft and the risk of injury to aircrew. The other problem to emerge was the need for a speed-up in flight-deck operations calling for simultaneous landing and take-off.

The angled flight-deck, offset between 5 degrees and 10 degrees, was in effect two decks in one. It allowed aircraft who missed the arrester wires to open up, accelerate away and then circuit for another approach

A British Scimitar is guided onto a steam catapult, prior to launching from HMS Ark Royal during the 1950s.

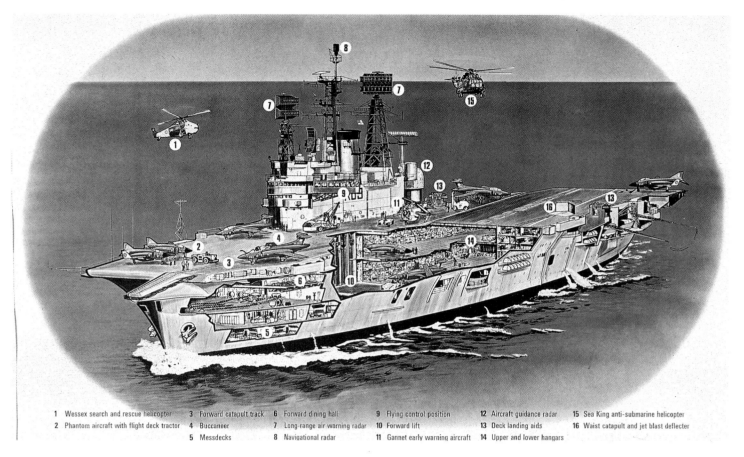

1	Wessex search and rescue helicopter	3	Forward catapult track	6	Forward dining hall	9	Flying control position	12	Aircraft guidance radar	15	Sea King anti-submarine helicopter
2	Phantom aircraft with flight deck tractor	4	Buccaneer	7	Long-range air warning radar	10	Forward lift	13	Deck landing aids	16	Waist catapult and jet blast deflecter
		5	Messdecks	8	Navigational radar	11	Gannet early warning aircraft	14	Upper and lower hangars		

A cut-away of HMS Ark Royal. It was the British who pioneered the angled flight-deck.

but simultaneously allowed the flight-deck to remain clear for take-off. This British idea was first incorporated in the conversion of USS *Antietam*, after successful trials had been carried out on a simulated angled deck, painted on HMS *Triumph* and USS *Midway*.

Towards the end of the war many carrier aircraft had become too heavy for a conventional take-off so that launching by catapult became almost routine. When postwar take-off weights increased to a point where existing catapults, even using hydraulics, cordite or pneumatics, could no longer cope, an ingenious new system was devised by the Royal Navy. Steam from the ship's boilers is drawn into two parallel cylinders below the deck and drives a shuttle down each cylinder. The thrust is controlled by a special launching valve which regulates itself according to the weight of each aircraft, ensuring that it attains the correct launching speed. The bridle attaching the aircraft to a launching hook falls away on take-off.

As landing speeds continued to increase, it became more and more difficult for the landing control officer, or 'batman', to judge the approach speed of an aircraft and, as early as 1949, another British team was working on an automatic landing system – the MLS (Mirror Landing Sight). The

MLS is mounted on the port side of the flight-deck and is essentially a row of lights reflected by a large curved mirror. This produces a pattern that is visible only to a pilot coming in with his wings level and at the right height. A later refinement has been the translation of air speed into sound: a single note, heard through the pilot's headset, eliminates the need for a constant check on the air speed indicator.

Enormous advances in jet aircraft performance called for new designs in carriers. When its light fleet carriers found it increasingly difficult to fly-off jet aircraft, the United States embarked on the construction of a new generation of super carriers, jet-age giants capable of handling aircraft with a launch weight of 36.6 tons (37.2 tonnes) [including a nuclear payload of 5.3 tons (5.4 tonnes)]. The *Forrestal*, CVAN 59, an attack carrier completed in 1955, was to be the first of seven. Second only in size to the 64,800-ton (65,800-tonne) Japanese *Shinano* of 1944, she displaced 59,000 tons (60,000 tonnes), had an overall length of 1,086 ft (331 m) and four shaft-geared turbines that generated 280,000 shp, giving her a fleet speed of 33 knots. The *Forrestal* operated between 70 and 85 aircraft and carried a crew of 4,940. No longer was the carrier's role to seek out and destroy an enemy fleet, for at that time no such fleet existed. Lessons learned in the Korean War underlined the need for a projection of power ashore to ensure a localized superiority – it was hoped that the *Forrestal* with her 4.5 acres (1.8 hectares) of deck space would supply this.

Once the first nuclear-powered submarine, USS *Nautilus*, proved successful, with virtually unlimited range and high speeds, it was agreed that the fifth super carrier, CVAN 65, should be powered by eight water-cooled reactors, generating an 'admitted' 280,000 shp, to produce a fleet speed of 35 knots. The 'Big E', USS *Enterprise*, was a colossus, displacing 76,000 tons (77,200 tonnes) with an overall length of 1,123 ft (342.3 m), a crew of 5,500 and carrying 84 aircraft. Her cruising range was governed only by those of the ships in company with her.

From the carriers of the U.S. Seventh Fleet in the Gulf of Tonkin, the U.S. Navy maintained a secure air base for operations over both North and South Vietnam. At the height of the Vietnam War there were six carriers on station with a total of 450 aircraft. Navy aircraft and helicopters also operated from shore bases; large numbers of helicopters operated with the Navy's riverine force of small boats in the Mekong Delta.

The introduction of the McDonnell F4 in 1961 gave the U.S. Navy both a first-class fighter and a strike aircraft. It was the mainstay of carrier operations during the conflict in Vietnam. It flew both MigCAP (Combat Air Patrol) missions and bombing missions. It was in a F4J from the USS *Constellation* that Lieutenant Randall Cunningham and his radar intercept officer, Lieutenant Driscoll, became the first aces of the war, when they shot down three enemy Mig 17 fighters. They were forced to parachute into the Gulf of Tonkin as a result of air combat but were quickly picked up and returned to the carrier as heroes.

The RA-5C photo-reconnaissance version of the A-5B Vigilante was used to supply detailed results of bombing missions and to identify enemy targets. This type of aircraft was also used to photograph, in great detail, the whole of Vietnam which

A batman brings in an aircraft aboard USS Wasp during the Second World War. With the coming of the jet aircraft, electronic aids were needed to land the much faster new generation of naval aircraft.

An F4 Phantom pilot waits for the launch signal aboard USS Constellation *in the South China Sea during the Vietnam War.*

allowed the Americans to produce accurate maps of both the North and South.

The war also saw the first use of the nuclear-powered carrier in combat. The USS *Enterprise* (CVAN 65) which had been commissioned in November 1961 was the first warship ever to be built with no armament. Electronics and aircraft were her only defence. She had the largest suite of radars and electronic countermeasures (ECM) of any vessel afloat. Unlike conventional carriers which need vast quantities of fuel, the *Enterprise*'s nuclear reactor gave limitless power. Her first set of nuclear rods lasted three years and in that time she travelled 207,000 miles.

As the air war over North Vietnam intensified U.S. air losses rose dramatically. The Army and Marines demanded the reactivation of the battleship *New Jersey*. She was recommissioned at a cost of $21

million which compared favourably with the cost of replacing six shot-down F4s.

Intelligence officers identified over 1,000 targets which the *New Jersey* was able to hit but which had previously only been in range of strike aircraft. During her tour of duty in the South China Sea in 1968–69, the *New Jersey* fired 5,688 rounds, compared with 771 rounds between 1943 and 1945.

The last act of the Seventh Fleet during the Vietnam conflict was the evacuation of Saigon. Seventy helicopters flew 630 sorties and airlifted 1,373 Americans, 5,595 South Vietnamese and 85 'third country' nationals to waiting ships. So many helicopters took part that, in the end, as helicopters landed and emptied their human cargoes, the helicopters were pushed over the side so that the next one could land.

Aircrew check ordnance loads on their Grumman Intruder aircraft aboard USS Ranger (CVAN-61), before a mission over North Vietnam.

A dramatic view from the rear cockpit of a Grumman F14A Tomcat, as two other Tomcats fly in close formation.

A *bird's-eye view, of USS Dwight D. Eisenhower (CVN 69), the second of the 'Nimitz' class nuclear-powered multi-role aircraft carriers, the largest carriers ever built.*

In 1975 the Americans brought the nuclear-powered USS *Nimitz* into commission. With a displacement of 82,000 tons (83,300 tonnes), she was even bigger than the 'Big E', though her overall length of 1,092 ft (333 m) was slightly shorter. With her 90-aircraft capacity, *Nimitz* had originally been designated CVAN, meaning nuclear attack carrier; however, rocketing costs forced her and her proposed sister ships, *Dwight D. Eisenhower* and *Carl Vinson*, to be commissioned as multi-mission (CVN) carriers, reducing their attack potential by including anti-submarine aircraft within their complements. The cost played a decisive part in the change of direction of seaborne air power, as did the Soviet expansion into an all-purpose navy. The final cost of *Nimitz* was $1.8 billion and the cost of her two sister ships topped the $2-billion mark. The United States simply could not afford such figures and NATO allies were even more financially restricted; new methods of attaining airborne superiority at sea had to be sought.

The Role of Helicopters

The helicopter first made its appearance in the latter stages of the Second World War as a crude affair used mainly for U-Boat spotting and air-sea rescue (ASR). It was not until the Korean War that its potential was realized. During this conflict the Americans finally developed it as a vertical assault weapon, having previously used it only for transport and communications. The potential of helicopters led them to convert the CVE *Thetis Bay* into a helicopter-assault ship in 1955, which, following the practical demonstration of the value of assault helicopters at Suez, became the forerunner of many such ships.

The Anglo-French Suez operation of 1956 highlighted, in real terms, the value of helicopter-assault carriers. They had formed a complete mobile task force, used to deal with limited wars or 'brush fires' and capable of rapidly landing troops, equipment and transport.

Trouble began when President Nasser of

Egypt denied Israeli ships entrance to the Suez Canal. War broke out between the two countries and Great Britain and France, to whom the canal was a vital lifeline to the East, intervened with a joint ultimatum which was ignored. France for some time had been operating four carriers obtained from Great Britain and the United States because her own two which were under construction, the *Clemenceau* and *Foch*, were not ready in time for the Suez adventure. This amphibious operation was undertaken by the two countries against Egypt. Without the advantage of a land base, it proved to be a model operation, blue-printing future strategy. Aircraft from six carriers quickly eliminated Egyptian air opposition, allowing the Royal Marine Commandos to land and establish a bridgehead for a large-scale Anglo-French parachute 'drop'. When the third Commando went in by 'helo', it established a precedent that has since been extended to become the accepted method of dealing with 'brush fires'. The successful conclusion of the operation was curtailed by world opinion and a United Nations Force took over but, nonetheless, the carrier force emerged from the action with great credit. The helicopter was shown to be a perfect machine for flying ashore a limited number of highly trained assault troops.

Royal Navy Wessex helicopters prepare to carry Royal Marine Commandos during the Suez action. This was the first time that helicopters had been used in this type of action.

Today the helicopter has taken over duties formerly carried out by fixed-wing aircraft, notably in an anti-submarine role, both location and destruction. Armed with bombs, torpedoes and the emerging guided missile, helicopters make a powerful fleet weapon, a fact which was more than proved during the Falklands Campaign. One of the larger helicopters, the Westland Sea King, is a complete weapons system in itself. Neither as fast, nor as far-reaching as a fixed-wing aircraft, the Sea King, however, has the virtue of flying sufficiently slowly to be able to trail an underwater sonar which can detect a submarine, either by bouncing ultrasonic sound waves off the enemy's hull, or by listening for propeller noise. A heavy aircraft, weighing over 9 tons (9 tonnes), she is roomy enough to carry extensive detection equipment, a payload of homing torpedoes and depth charges, as well as her crew of four. Two Rolls Royce Gnome engines give her a speed of 161 mph (259 km/h). Even when operating at slower speeds, she is far faster than any submarine, which allows her to keep pace with an escaping enemy.

The threat posed by the spiralling Soviet submarine construction programme caused carriers to become more and more concerned with AS (Anti-Submarine) warfare. The appearance of the Soviet underwater ballistic missile SS-N4 (Sark) in the late 1950s, fired from a submarine, was a technological breakthrough that further influenced the development of the carrier. The ever-increasing threat from Soviet submarines was serious enough to cause the U.S. Navy to convert most of her 'Essex' class to CVSs, anti-submarine carriers, which became the nucleus of Hunter-Killer groups – HUKs.

As emphasis on anti-submarine warfare increased, escort ships were fitted with helicopter pads, extending yet again the fleet's AS potential. All today's frigates and destroyers carry at least one all-purpose helicopter. Because of the necessarily small helicopters carried by escort ships, capable only of either detection or attack, a new breed of ship came into being, the helicopter cruiser, which could operate heavier, more sophisticated helicopters. The Italians were first in the field with the *Andrea Doria,* a 6,500-ton (6,600-tonne) missile-armed cruiser, operating four helicopters; she was followed by the *Vittorio Veneto* which was able to house nine. Other countries followed suit, among them Great Britain who could see a more economical means of increasing her seaborne air power. It was during this time that the Soviet Union built its first aircraft carrier. Although not a carrier in the strict sense of the word, the hybrid 15,000-ton (15,240-tonne) *Moskva,* with her heavy missile armament, also operates a squadron of 18 AS helicopters.

Above: A Royal Navy Sea King built by Westland Helicopters. The Royal Navy uses its Sea Kings in a variety of roles including the ferrying of men and equipment, but its main task is anti-submarine warfare. Following the Falklands War a small number of them have been fitted with an airborne early warning radar to provide cover for carrier operations.

Opposite: A U.S. Navy SH-3A Sea King helicopter lowers its sonar dome during an anti-submarine mission. The use of helicopters in this type of role extends the all-round protection of naval task forces.

A spectacular view of a Soviet Hormone *helicopter against the setting sun.*

75

Opposite: The 'Invincible' class carrier was designed as a helicopter-carrying 'through-deck' cruiser. With the development of the BAe Sea Harrier, this was changed and a 'ski jump' was added to aid take off. HMS Invincible *saw service in the Falklands.*

Left: A Marine Corps AV8B Harrier prepares to land on a U.S. carrier. The AV8B has been jointly developed by McDonnell Douglas and British Aerospace.

V/STOL

The escalating cost of fleet carriers and the limited attack value of the helicopter called for a change of direction and a concept as revolutionary as the exploding shell was to the naval gun. Great Britain developed the Vertical/Short Take-Off and Landing aircraft, the V/STOL. This revolutionary strike/fighter aircraft, finalized in the Hawker Sea Harrier with a speed of 737 mph (1,186 km/h), is able to lift-off vertically from a deck, requiring neither catapult nor arrester gear. Such a take-off, however costly in fuel, reduced the aircraft's pay load, but by ensuring a short running take-off, especially with an inclined deck, its attack potential was greatly increased. It took an order for three Harrier squadrons from the U.S. Marines, who were quick to evaluate the Harrier's enormous potential, to overcome political opposition in Britain and ensure the Sea Harrier entering service in the Royal Navy. The confidence of the American Marines was fully justified by the performance of Harriers in the Falklands, where they shot down 20 faster Argentinian aircraft, without suffering a single casualty in air-to-air combat.

It did not take the Soviets long to appreciate the value of the Harrier, and in a very short time they were producing their own version of a V/STOL aircraft, to operate from a 'Kiev' class carrier, a true carrier in every sense, complete with angled flight-deck. This 40,000-ton (40,640-tonne) carrier, although no match for the American super carriers, is an immensely powerful ship, with a speed of around 30 knots. Seen chiefly as an AS carrier, she has over 20 search-and-destroy helicopters as a first line of attack, backed up by 10 to 15 V/STOL Yak-36s (*Forgers*), for ship defence and limited strike capacity. *Kiev* also bristles with detection equipment and missile launchers able to deliver a nuclear payload up to 250 miles (400 km).

The mounting cost of super carriers and the emergence of satellite-directed missiles has put the future form of the carrier into the balance, but one way or another naval air power still has a vital role to play in sea warfare.

Equipped with Aphid AA-8 air-to-air missiles, these two Yak-38 fighter aircraft are parked, at the ready, on the deck of a Soviet aircraft carrier.

OCEAN LINERS

The coming of steam opened up travel and drew the world together, making it a much smaller place. On land the steam train enabled people who had never been further than the next town or village to travel the extent of their country and beyond. Eating habits changed; fresh meat and farm produce and fish from the coast could be transported quickly. New lands could be opened up. The steam ship extended man's horizons even further. By opening up the seas and oceans, distant lands, once months away, could be reached in days.

Sea travel became big business; people clamoured to cross the Atlantic both ways, some as passengers others as immigrants seeking a better life in the New World. Both offered big profits, the one paying well for luxurious comfort, the other willing to put up with discomfort and dense overcrowding to escape from the misery of their lot in Europe.

The earlier passenger ships were somewhat less than luxurious but by the turn of the century men such as Edward Knight Collins, owner of the Dramatic Line, and Samuel Cunnard had – at enormous cost to the passenger – introduced some grandeur and speed to the transatlantic crossing and competition for the Blue Riband was on. At the other end of the scale, however, was the desperately poor immigrant who was prepared to put up with sordid, unhealthy, often dangerous conditions aboard sailing packets to reach the promised land. It was not the social reformers, humanitarians or sympathetic governments who relieved the lot of these immigrants, but hard-headed businessmen, such as William Inman, who went into the trade for a fat profit. Inman was a partner in the Quaker line of Richardson Brothers. By making the immigrants' passages tolerable – seeing that they had reasonable accommodation and feed-

ing them decently – he ensured that they arrived in New York fit and healthy. Thus his vessels, free from quarantine restrictions, enjoyed a rapid turnaround.

The Cunard Line

The name Cunard, however, stands out in the story of Atlantic sea travel. From its early beginnings as the British and North American Royal Mail Steam Packet Company, operating four wooden paddle steamers, the Cunard Line has collected first place after first place, and an unassailable string of Blue Ribands (44) from both east and west crossings. The company's first modest 1,154-ton (1,172-tonne) Britannia of 1840 grew into the mighty 83,673-ton (85,012-tonne) Queen Elizabeth, launched in 1938, the largest liner every built. In 1840 the 207-ft (63-m) long Britannia carried 150 passengers; the Queen Elizabeth, a hundred years later, had accommodation for over 2,200.

From the outset, the Halifax, Nova Scotia-born merchant and shipowner, Samual Cunnard, established a reputation for safety and reliability for his line, as these instructions, handed to his first steamship commander of Britannia, Captain Woodruff, illustrate. 'It will be obvious to you that it is of first importance to the partners of the Britannia that she attains a character for speed and safety.' Indeed the line picked up 28 Blue Ribands from 1840 until the big German liners of the 'Kaiser Wilhelm der Grosse' class which held the title between 1897 and 1906.

The 'Kaiser Wilhelm der Grosse' class liners were the pride of Germany, carrying the largest engines afloat, displacing over 14,000 tons with a speed of 22.35 knots. Carrying 1,749 passengers they made the passage in just under six days.

The great liners rule the waves and Thomas Cook & Son handled all the world's travel requirements.

The first truly modern liner, Cunard's Mauritania, held the Blue Riband for 22 years. With an average speed of 27.4 knots, she easily took the 'Blue Ribbon' from Kaiser Wilhelm der Grosse.

Kaiser Wilhelm der Grosse	
Displacement	20,000 tons (20,320 tonnes)
Length	688.6 ft (210 m)
Engines	28,000 ihp
Speed	22.35 knots
Crossing time	5 days 22 hours 45 minutes
Passengers	1,749
Crew	450

Mauritania	
Displacement	43,000 tons (43,700 tonnes)
Length	762 ft (232 m)
Engines	68,000 shp
Speed	27.4 knots
Crossing time	4 days 20 hours 15 minutes
Passengers	2,335
Crew	812

The *Mauritania*

The first truly modern liner was the Cunard Line's *Mauritania*. When she and her sister ship, the ill-fated *Lusitania*, appeared in 1907, they even dwarfed Germany's 'Kaiser Wilhelm der Grosse' class (which had been the largest, fastest and most modern liners to date) in size and outstripped them in performance. Everything about the new ships was a triumph of technology, setting a pattern for all the liners that followed.

The *Mauritania*'s hull was fabricated from thousands of high-tensile steel plates and she was powered by four steam turbine engines – the first to be given these – driving four gigantic screws. The engines were fired by 35 boilers, initially fed with coal. After the First World War, she was converted to oil. Cunard increased the margins of damage control by being the first to install a watertight door system controlled from the bridge.

A few months after her maiden voyage, the *Mauritania* captured the famous Blue Riband for a record-breaking westward voyage, Liverpool to New York, a record she held for the next 22 years averaging 25.5 knots on 27 consecutive voyages. Her total reliability has never been surpassed. Her sister ship *Lusitania* was not so lucky. She was sunk in May 1915 by *U.20* off Kinsale in Southern Ireland on a return trip.

The *Titanic*

Unfortunately, as ships improved technically beyond recognition, their administration did not, and safety precautions in particular sadly lagged behind. The Board of Trade and its foreign equivalents stated in the Merchant Shipping Acts that the number of lifeboats carried should be based on a ship's tonnage. They laid down regulations for ships up to 10,000 tons (10,160 tonnes) which should carry 16 lifeboats on davits, accommodating about 1,000 passengers. No one saw fit to alter this ruling as ships grew beyond 10,000 tons, with a comparable increase in passenger numbers; it took a fearful tragedy to have the safety regulations tightened up.

On her maiden voyage, 48 hours from a traditional New York fireboat welcome, the 46,328-ton (47,069-tonne) *Titanic*, pride of the White Star Line, hit an iceberg at 22 knots. It was on the pitch-black night of 14 April 1912 that an unseen mountain of black ice sliced down her starboard bow opening up three compartments to the sea. Within minutes they were flooded and the supposedly unsinkable *Titanic* was doomed; nothing could be done to save her – her captain sent out an SOS and hoped. Only 1,187 passengers, mainly women and children, scrambled aboard the lifeboats; there was no space for more. At 0220 hours, lights still blazing, the mighty ship slipped under by the head to settle on the bottom, over 12,000 ft (3,660 m) below, taking with her 1,490 passengers and crew.

Now, 74 years later, a multi-million-dollar scheme has been proposed to raise the *Titanic* from her watery grave. She has already been located and remarkable underwater colour photographs show her lying in a bed of shale off the Grand Banks some way to the southeast of her last incorrect SOS position. The photographs also reveal that she has remained in astonishingly good condition, a hemp line lies in its correct position and intact across her forecastle anchor chains amid undisturbed bollards and machinery. Another photograph clearly shows a large crane, which must have broken away from the stern deck as the stricken ship went under, lying some distance from the ship's hull.

One of the Mauritania's *turbine engines being assembled at the Cammell Laird shipyard at Birkenhead. The* Mauritania *was the first passenger liner to be powered by steam turbine engines.*

Trapped under it is what appears to be a human ribcage and other bones, with an Edwardian lady's hat and button boot nearby.

A salvage expert, John Pierce, has put forward a startling plan for bringing the *Titanic* to the surface, providing the necessary millions can be raised for the venture. Using two free-swimming, manned sub- mersibles which will be able to withstand the incredible pressure experienced at that depth, he proposes to use inflatable bags to raise the ship. Rolled up like carpets, these tear-shaped lifting bags will be positioned along each side of the hull at regular intervals by the submersibles. Once in position, watertight seals on the bags will be activated by an ultrasonic signal from

The ill-fated Titanic *begins her tragic maiden voyage from Southampton on 10 April 1912. The lack of lifeboats was a major cause of the huge loss of life.*

the salvage ship above, allowing the sea water to come into contact with a chemical contained inside. This will generate vast quantities of hydrogen, sufficient, in the view of John Pierce, to inflate the bags and slowly lift the *Titanic* to the surface. Already this method has been used successfully to salvage the Greenpeace ship *Rainbow* from the bottom of Auckland harbour.

However, raising an ocean liner lying more than 2 miles (3 km) below the surface of the water is altogether more daunting.

Already moral issues have been raised. Should the drowned be left to lie in peace? A precedent has been set by the decision not to tamper with HMS *Royal Oak* lying in Scapa Flow; she is to remain undisturbed, a war grave.

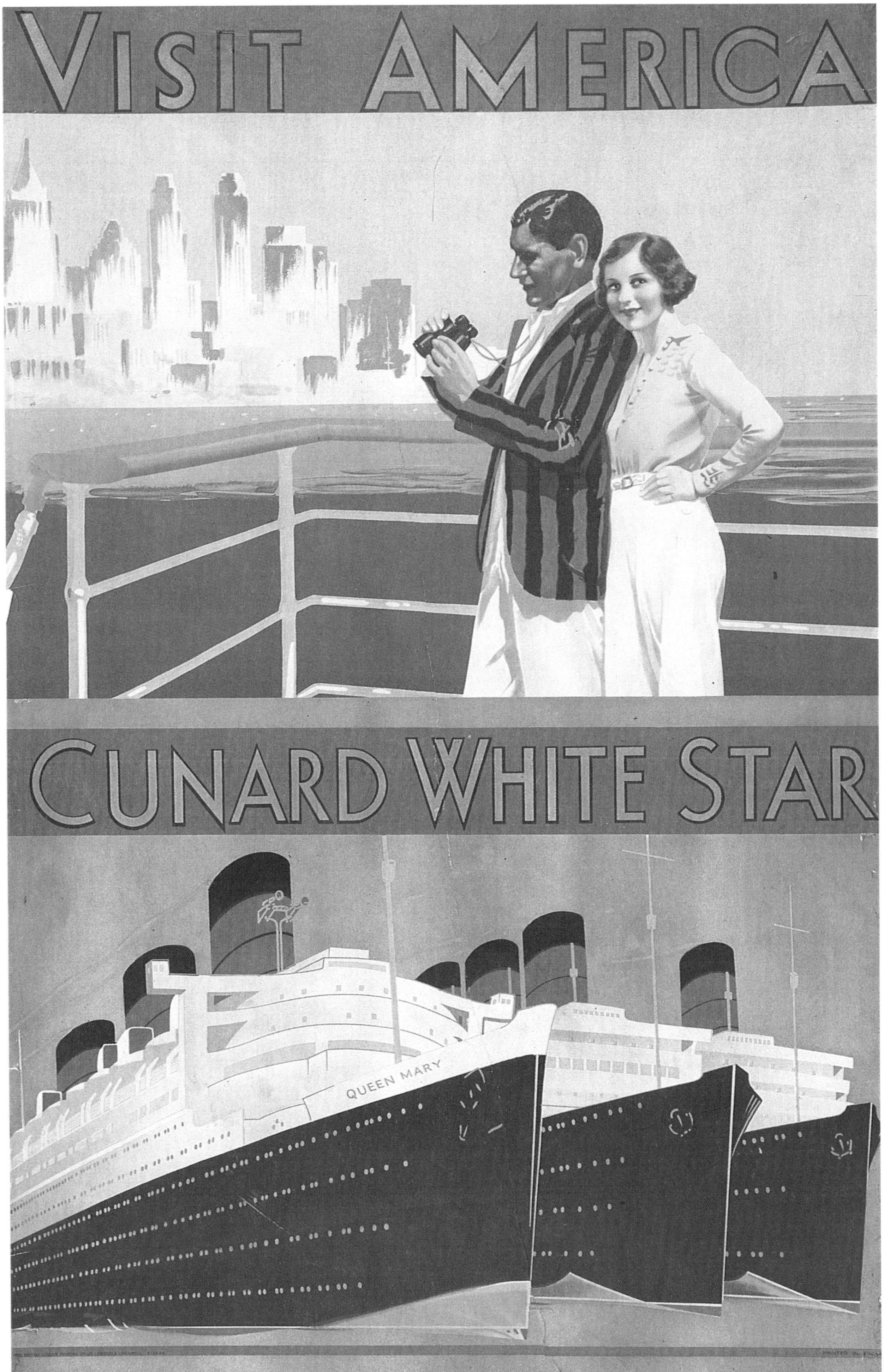
VISIT AMERICA
CUNARD WHITE STAR
QUEEN MARY

Cunard and Its Competitors

But even the *Titanic*'s fate did not deter passengers from making transatlantic journeys and did not stop companies from making those journeys as comfortable and as fast as possible.

'Getting there is half the fun', Cunard's slogan, sums up the heyday of the transatlantic liners in the 1920s and 1930s. Liners became larger and larger, reaching unparalleled sizes, and with an increasing demand for luxury and convenience, Atlantic liners truly became cities at sea.

Competition however grew fierce and in 1929 the North German Lloyd Lines at last wrested away the Blue Riband from Cunard's *Mauritania*, with a four-day 14-hour 30-minute crossing averaging 27.92 knots. The *Bremen*, a sleek, streamlined, 50,000-ton (50,800-tonne) vessel with two squat, raking funnels, was a complete break with the past. Her 123,000-hp engines gave her a top speed of 28.5 knots and she carried a crew of 990. The German designers talked of purity of form, laying great stress on the forward overlapping of the hull plates to lessen resistance to the water. There is more than a hint of growing German nationalism to be seen in Professor de Groot's introduction to the sales brochure for the *Bremen*. 'The architecture of the *Bremen* emancipates us from a time which is not our own, and leads us into the grandeur of our present age, in which we desire to breathe and not to suffocate.'

Unfortunately the reign of the *Bremen* and her sister ship was short-lived when in 1933 the Italian liner *Rex* captured the Blue Riband, to have it, in turn, rudely snatched away from her just over a year later by the French *Normandie*. The *Normandie* was more than a ship – she was a piece of France. Her cuisine was unexcelled, the table wine free; she had swimming pools, a winter garden, a theatre and a public room that could seat 1,000 people. She was the first liner to exceed 1,000 ft (305 m) in length – 1,029 ft (314 m) – this was later exceeded by the *Queen Elizabeth*, but only by 2 ft (0.6 m) – and she had a gross tonnage of 82,799 (84,124 tonnes), which was to be bettered only by the *Queen Elizabeth*.

On her maiden voyage the *Normandie* took the Blue Riband, which she relinquished the following year, 1936, to the *Queen Mary*, but she continued to operate as an Atlantic express liner until the fall of France in 1940.

The Americans, who considered the French to be doubtful allies, seized the *Normandie* following the attack on Pearl Harbor and converted her into a troopship, renamed USS *Lafayette* – her French crew left the ship singing the French National Anthem. Before the crew departed, a United States Coast Guard captain had come aboard to protect the ship from sabotage. Commandant Hervé Le Huédé, after stating that he and his crew would never sabotage the *Normandie*, remarked, '.. But if we wanted to do it, nothing would be easier; all we should have to do would be to leave the ship and hand her over to you' – and such proved to be the case.

Opposite: Cunard's liners led the rest of the world's passenger fleets on the Atlantic crossing, and the two 'Queens' of the White Star line led the fleet.

The Normandie's *first-class dining room. The food was the finest that France's best chefs could offer.*

At 1437 hours on 9 February 1942, thousands of kapok life jackets dumped in the main saloon caught fire, probably started by a spark from an acetylene torch. Within minutes it was a blazing inferno, the situation hardly helped by the fact that the direct line to the New York Fire Brigade was out of order. When they at last began pumping water into her, 3,500 tons (3,560 tonnes) of it, the water froze and the *Normandie* capsized. Eventually righted, she was towed away by 15 tugs and finally sold for scrap.

The 'Queens'

In 1934 the Cunard Line commissioned the first of the 'Queens' in reply to the *Normandie*, the *Queen Mary*. Fractionally smaller (her length was 1,019 ft, 311 m), she had a gross tonnage of 81,237 tons (82.537 tonnes). The *Queen Mary* was faster than the *Normandie*, averaging 31.69 knots on one Blue Riband run. Four years later Cunard brought out the biggest liner of all, the 83,673-ton (85,011-tonne) *Queen Elizabeth*, but as the Second World

Opposite: The opulence of the main first-class lounge of the Queen Mary, *probably the most famous liner of them all.*

Both the Queen Mary (top), *and the* Queen Elizabeth (bottom) *were requisitioned for the duration of the Second World War. Carrying troops and vital supplies, they had sufficient speed to allow them to outrun the U-Boat packs.*

ORIENT LINE CRUISES

Managers: Anderson, Green & Co., Ltd.   5 Fenchurch Avenue, London, E.C.3

Opposite: If Cunard ruled the Atlantic, then the route to the East belonged to P & O. Here, a P & O liner passes through the Suez Canal, en route to Australia.

P & O passengers enjoy the delights of a swimming pool. The pool became a 'must' aboard luxury liners.

War had begun, she started her life as a troopship, able to accommodate 8,200 troops. Between them, the *Queen Elizabeth* and the *Queen Mary* carried 320,000 of the 850,000 American troops ferried to Europe and, although a target for U-Boats, they both came through the war unscathed.

Passage East

Passage East was never as glamorous as the Atlantic run, with less cut-glass and glitter and far more simple menus, but by and large accommodation was more spacious. Whereas the transatlantic passenger, in the main, travelled for pleasure, simply to visit Europe or North America, and was prepared to pay for luxury, passengers travelling to the East were usually on their way to take up appointments and postings, or begin a new life. Unlike the Atlantic there was no Blue Riband for the Eastern trip; an hour or so off the journey was of no significance, though ships had to be fast to attract the trade.

Gradually, as the 19th century drew on, the romantic, graceful clippers gave way to coal-burning ships as steamship lines pushed their services further eastwards, firstly to India, then on to China and Australia. Uninhibited by the need for fuel, sailing ships could afford to round the

The P & O Canberra was converted from luxury liner to troopship for the Falklands War. A helicopter pad was built over the open-air swimming pool.

Cape of Good Hope, but it took time – the famous race between the *Ariel* and *Taiping* from China to England took 99 days. On the other hand, the need to take on coal at regular intervals made such a journey uneconomical for steamers. Other routes for reaching the East were soon discovered.

As Cunard dominated the Atlantic, so P & O, the Peninsular and Oriental Line, became the household name in shipping to the East. Starting as the Peninsular Steam Navigation Company plying between England and Spain and Portugal, it was persuaded to open up a passenger service to India via Egypt. Winning the Royal Mail contract made eastern passenger trade an economic proposition, and a service was laid on to Alexandria, where mail and passengers were transported overland across Egypt to Suez to pick up the 1,974-ton (2,006-tonne) paddle steamer *Bentinck* for the passage to India. Even when the Suez Canal was opened the British Post Office at first insisted on the mail being transported overland by train until the use of the Canal was proved to be quicker. Despite these problems, by 1870 the voyage from Southampton to Australia had been cut to 57 days; today the trip takes three weeks.

The Line went from strength to strength, its ships growing ever bigger in size culminating in the 44,807-ton (45,524-tonne) *Canberra* built in 1961. But she was to be the last liner built for passenger service alone. The introduction of the jumbo jet, which doubled the number of passengers that could be carried by an aircraft, spelled a decline in the economic practicability of a regular passenger service and forced a move to be made towards the tourist trade and cruise liners. These cruise liners, such as the 17,500-ton (17,780-tonne) *Spirit of London*, as in the case of Atlantic liners were designed for a different role. Slower, 21 knots as opposed to the 27-knot *Canberra*, they became far more luxurious with only a single class, every cabin having its own bathroom facilities.

As cruise liners become smaller in size, the problem of transporting troops, should another incident like the Falklands occur, flares up. In 1982 the P & O *Canberra* was ideal for the task. Arriving at 0900 hours in Southampton 7 April, after a world cruise, her 1,650 passengers were hurried ashore, to be replaced by a team of workmen anxious to get on with the task of converting her into a troopship – the deadline was the evening of 8 April, 36 hours away. In that time, among other things, two prefabricated helicopter flight-decks had to be installed, one over the Bonito swimming pool, the other over the observation deck forward of the bridge. Not all the prefabricated parts were delivered on time, which put back her sailing by a day. Nevertheless, she sailed on 9 April, with construction work still going on, and she was well out to sea before her helicopters were in use. Still painted white, she was soon affectionately christened the 'Great White Whale'. With the Falklands experience in mind, will the modern cruise liners be able to offer a similar facility?

Overleaf: A beautiful aerial view of the Cunard liner, Queen Elizabeth II, underway.

Postwar Transatlantic Trade

By 1946 most of the big passenger ships had been reconverted from their wartime roles as troopships and armed merchant cruisers, and countries began once more to compete for sea tourist trade. Holland, Italy, Greece and Sweden built new ships, but none was as large or as fast as the prewar giants. It was left to the U.S.A. to launch a liner of surpassing distinction, the *United States.* For the next ten years, the transatlantic passenger trade enjoyed a boom and the *United States* went into service right in the middle of it. She was a 53,330 tonner (54,183 tonnes) and cost a fortune to build – $77,000,000. However, four-sevenths of this cost was offset by the U.S. government, which saw her primarily as a troopship in time of war. The fastest liner ever built – she is reputed to have bettered 40 knots, during her trials – she became the last liner to capture the Blue Riband: three days ten hours 40 minutes at a speed of 35.59 knots. She was also the first ship to have her superstructure fabricated in aluminium alloy.

By then the writing was on the wall for the express transatlantic liner. When the giant four-engined bombers were converted into passenger aircraft, it removed the incentive to compete for the Blue Riband. There was no competition; passengers in a hurry, particularly when the jet engine was introduced into civil aviation, could now cross the Atlantic in hours as opposed to days by ship. Shipping lines had to take a hard look at the market and come up with a solution. It was soon apparent that amalgamating with airlines was not the answer, but a number of facts emerged that did point towards a possible solution. One interesting fact was that a hard core of passengers, as much as six per cent, preferred to travel by ship. This, coupled with the growing boom in tourism, gave the ocean liners a new lease on life, but not the

Following a major refit by new owners, the SS France, renamed SS Norway, cruises through the Caribbean Islands.

Passengers enjoy an outdoor feast during a holiday cruise. Eating is still a major event on board luxury liners.

giant ones; by the mid-1960s they were found to be uneconomical. The 'Queens' and their sister giants went out of commission to be replaced by dual-purpose ships –

but not before one final twitch of the tail.

The *France* was to be the pride of her country – at her launching General de Gaulle said, 'May this ship accomplish her destiny', as his wife sent her on her way with a Nebuchadnezzar (equivalent to about 20 bottles) of champagne – but by the time of her maiden voyage she was something of an anachronism. The last of the truly express Atlantic liners, destined to make 34 round voyages a year alone, she found the competition from the air too fierce, and when, in 1975, government subsidy became prohibitively costly, she was removed from service.

Since the *France*, only one big dual-purpose ship has been built, the *Queen Elizabeth II*. Although smaller than her fellow 'Queens', at 67,000 tons (68,100 tonnes), she is still a big ship, but one designed to operate as a transatlantic liner in the summer months, and as a luxury holiday cruise liner in the winter. She is indeed the complete floating holiday centre – at a price! Now that the need for speed has been eliminated, the accent is clearly on opulence and entertainment.

Her four restaurants all command a five-star rating, two of them five-star plus; she boasts six glittering bars and a theatre seating 531. There is drive-on accommodation for 70 cars and each cabin is served by its own steward and stewardess. Entertainment is lavish and comprehensive – gymnasiums, jacuzzi and sauna, golf driving nets, casino, library, radio, film and a complete shopping centre with every facility.

What better way to spend your day than relaxing by the pool. As in the 1930s, the swimming pool is still an important feature of modern cruise liners.

Queen Elizabeth II	
Gross tonnage	67,139 (68,213 tonnes)
Length	963 ft (293 m)
Speed	28.5 knots
Horse power	110,000 hp from three boilers
Propellers	2 six-bladed
Deck space	4,500 sq yd (3,760 sq m)
Number of decks	13
Passengers	1,850
Crew	1,000

While the Boeing 747 now rules the Atlantic crossing New York and Southampton have declined in importance as passenger ports, the role of the liner has changed to become that of a floating hotel. In the West Indian and Caribbean ports, the demand for berths has led to major redevelopment of harbours. New designs for ships that resemble floating multi-storey hotels are on the drawing boards and these ships will provide every bedroom cabin with a clear seaview. It is the Scandinavian lines who are leading the way in this type of luxury holiday and are offering the quality that went out with the great Blue Riband ships.

The Soviet Union was not slow in spotting a way to earn enormous sums of hard foreign currency and has developed a large fleet of tour liners. Each year thousands of passengers cruise both the Baltic and Mediterranean seas under the Soviet flag.

The rise of the Soviet cruise liners has allowed thousands of holiday makers to take a cruise holiday. A Soviet liner prepares to leave Tangiers on a cruise of the Mediterranean.

MERCHANT SHIPPING

Trade Follows the Flag

With the establishment of colonies by seafaring nations came the founding of large trading corporations, a cornerstone in the vast edifice of sea trade and the beginning of modern shipping companies. The discovery of new lands naturally led to the discovery of new commodities – cotton, tobacco, rice, fruits, spice, rubber and, more recently, oil. In exchange for these commodities, European maritime countries exported coal, iron and manufactured goods. This was especially true when the industrial revolution gripped Europe creating an ever-increasing demand for raw materials and a need to export manufactured goods. The coming of steam not only drew the world together, but opened up new markets and considerably extended the old ones. Cargoes once considered commercially unviable suddenly became commercially desirable and capable of making big profits.

Although cargo vessels never showed the same dramatic increase in size as passenger liners, they nonetheless became bigger during the second half of the 19th century and certainly increased in number. Towards the end of the century single-cargo vessels were beginning to appear, specialist ships designed to handle a specific commodity. Cargoes began to become known by the character of their contents. A cargo composed of a number of commodities which were loaded aboard at different ports and destined for several unloading ports was known as a 'general cargo'. This conjures up a picture not only of a ship from the Orient bearing spices, rubber, rice and exotic fruits, but of poet John Masefield's dirty British coaster, with its cargo of 'Tyne coal, road rails, pig iron, red lead and cheap tin trays'.

A single commodity, such as lumber or cotton, loaded on a ship became known as a 'special cargo' and when such a cargo was transported in great quantities or at special times of the year it was called 'special trade'. A 'bulk cargo' was a special cargo with particular properties, one that could only be handled – loaded or unloaded – *en masse* and for one reason or another could not be shipped with other commodities. Grain, coal, iron ore or fuel oil are examples of bulk cargoes.

The general design of merchant ships grew out of a need to preserve valuable cargo space at all costs. Originally a central bridge or 'island' was placed across the paddle wheels. This structure remained when screws replaced the paddles, as it was found to be an ideal position from which to control the ship. A steering position aft supplied a second 'island' and the third was created when a forecastle deck was added to house the crew and increase the cargo-carrying capacity of the ship and, incidentally, leave a clear deck for access to the holds.

By the turn of the century merchant ships had grown in size from around 2,000 tons (2,030 tonnes) to over 6,000 tons (6,100 tonnes). With the growing world demand for coal, not only for industrial and domestic use, but to establish coaling stations throughout the world for the expanding merchant fleets, colliers were becoming larger and already far-seeing designers were anticipating future trends. Isambard Kingdom Brunel introduced the first container ship when, in 1841, he loaded colliers from cubical iron boxes each containing 2½ tons of coal, which were lowered into the hold and the coal released through the bottom. He did not, however, think it through to the modern concept of leaving the containers on the ship. Roll-

A NASA-developed satellite beacon has been mounted on this modern representation of a fast clipper, the Pride of Baltimore.

on/roll-off ships were also anticipated in Thomas Dunn Marshall's *Bedlington* of 1842. 'The vessel is fitted on the floors with rails for waggons to be run fore and aft and calculated to contain 40 waggons, fitted with a working drop to answer either side over the main hatchway which is adapted to hoist and lower by the engine that drives the propelling screws which are fitted in each run. The boilers are placed close forward and the engines aft, leaving the entire hold amidships for the stowage of waggons on the four railways.'

In the second half of the 19th century, the specialist ship designed to carry a specific cargo began to appear. A refrigeration ship carried lamb carcasses from New Zealand to Britain in 1870 and 15 years later, the *Glaükauf*, the first tanker, put in an appearance. Previously oil had been shipped in barrels, but as this was found to be an uneconomic use of cargo space, the *Glaükauf* was designed so that the outer shell of the ship became the tank containing the oil.

Ports and Docks

Few ports are new and are, therefore, not totally able to deal efficiently with the ever-changing problems and requirements of water transport. Usually they 'developed' in natural harbours with an easy access to the hinterland, or at river estuaries, the accepted highways of commerce. Many of these river ports grew into great cities situated at points where the rivers could most conveniently be bridged: London, Glasgow, New York, San Francisco, Antwerp, Rotterdam and so on. More than a few of these ports are a trying legacy from the past, calling for enormous amounts of money to be spent on expensive dredging equipment and its operation to keep the ports workable.

Roughly speaking, ports can be split into six different types. Examples of each are listed below:

River ports: London, Bremen, Glasgow

Tidal ports: Liverpool, Antwerp

Natural harbours: San Francisco, New York, Sydney

Coastal ports: Valparaiso, Foochow, Madras

Canal ports: Panama, Port Said, Amsterdam

Delta ports: Rotterdam, Alexandria, Marseille

Natural ports have grown upon sites that have been adapted to anchoring and sheltering, the best known of which are in bays, such as Sydney and so on. Tidal ports invariably are river ports, but the reverse need not apply. With tidal ports the rise and fall of tide is so great that shipping has to be berthed in artificially constructed basins and docks with lock gates. Glasgow, on the other hand, with less tidal rise and fall, has riverside quays. Generally speaking, rivers that empty into sandy estuaries

The use of containers has changed the face of modern sea ports. Mixed cargoes can now safely be carried on the same ship.

need locks and docks and require constant dredging to keep the channels clear.

Rivers that enter the sea through a delta are not always the most practical ports from a shipping point of view; their channels are often meandering, narrow and need constant dredging. However, Rotterdam, the greatest port in the world, is a delta one. Whatever the type of port, there is a tremendous organizational back-up to ensure the speedy turnaround of ships, as merchantmen only make money when they are at sea. Thus cargo-handling has been speeded up by the use of forklift trucks, tractors, conveyor belts, straddle trucks, cranes and a host of other equipment, depending on the type of goods handled by a port. Most modern ports spread over an enormous area and coupled with the harbour facilities they are like small independent towns, serviced by a fleet of auxilliary vessels, tugs, dredgers, customs and pilot boats, lighters and safety attendance vessels.

Offshore Vessels and Tugs

Tugs, ever since their inception in the early 19th century, when they were used for towing wooden ships-of-the-line out of harbour when there was no wind, have been the mainstay of a port, fussing around liners and tankers, and towing lighters and barges. Generally they can be divided into two groups: short-haul tugs or ocean-going tugs. The small powerful vessels that operate in or near a harbour often generate up to 2,500 hp and have a tonnage of up to 250 tons (254 tonnes); they carry out general harbour duty and servicing. Long-haul tugs, on the other hand, are considerably larger, up to 2,000 tons (2,032 tonnes), generate 15,000 hp, and are steady seaworthy craft. They may be called upon to carry out such diverse operations as salvage work, the towage of ships and oil platforms or huge floating docks.

Offshore supply vessels and tugs are fast becoming the most numerous craft to be seen, especially as their sphere of operation becomes more and more extended. The technology that allowed the search for oil and gas to go further offshore into ever deeper water had much to do with the development of offshore vessels, a develop-

ment that has grown only in the last 20 years. As the number of rigs and platforms proliferate in steadily increasing numbers, more – and often more diverse – demands are being made on ocean-going tugs, supply and specialist support vessels; the building of multi-purpose, salvage, towage, supply and fire-fighting vessels is rapidly becoming the norm. These are supplemented by safety attendance vessels and research, oil-seeking vessels of which most, if not all, are fitted with helicopter pads.

The real workhorse of a port, however, is the dredger. In a continual battle to deepen harbours and channels, dredgers move thousands of tons of silt and sand every month, dumping it out to sea, far beyond the port entrance. The commonest form of dredger, the one most often seen working a port, is fitted with an endless chain of buckets which scoop up the bottom and deposit the contents of the buckets into lighters tied up alongside. These are then towed out to sea by tugs. Suction dredgers are sometimes used when the bottom is composed of soft mud or sand, and the more modern ones also incorporate a system of cutters to break up any harder ground into pieces sufficiently small to be accepted by the suction unit.

The MV Lady Harrison entered service with Racal Decca in 1984. She is the world's most advanced geophysical survey ship of her type. She is used by oil companies to gather vital information in their search for new oil fields.

103

The Expansion of the Mercantile Marine

At the turn of the century the continuing effect of the industrial revolution generated an enormous trade expansion and the number of ships over 100 tons registered worldwide in 1900 had risen to 29,093,728. By the outbreak of the First World War this had increased by 70 per cent to over 42,000,000 ships, of which Great Britain operated 45 per cent. Her nearest maritime rivals were the United States with 12 per cent and Germany with 10 per cent. However, the strength of Great Britain's merchant fleets also underlined her vulnerability. Whereas the United States was virtually self-sufficient in raw materials and saw its mercantile marine chiefly as an export arm, Great Britain depended on hers for her very existence with a need to import from all over the world. This left Britain wide open to a 'guerre de course', of which the German U-Boats soon took full advantage, and from which her armada of battleships was unable to protect her.

The general type of merchant ship of this period, even if specially designed to handle a particular commodity, was the 'three island' vessel, with four cargo holds, two foreward and two aft of a central bridge island. These were the ships – they appeared as three islands when hull down on the horizon – that became the chief victims of an all-out, no-holds-barred, U-Boat campaign. For the first time civilians (and merchantship crews were civilians) had been put into the frontline during a war. Losses were grave; 5,531 merchant vessels had been sunk representing over 13,000,000 tons (13,208,000 tonnes) of shipping, with Great Britain alone losing 2,480 ships. Despite a massive wartime shipbuilding programme, maritime countries found themselves woefully short of merchant ships to cope with the expected peacetime boom in world trade.

The manufacturing industries, turning even more to mass-production methods, were crying out for ships, still the main method of bulk transport, and for quicker, cheaper methods of getting ships onto the stocks. To replace ships sunk during the war as quickly as possible, fewer actual ships were built, but those that were built were of a greater tonnage than the previous ones, both cargo and passenger vessels.

New industrial products that emerged as a result of the war had a marked influence on the design of specialist ships. In particular advances made in the development of the internal-combustion engine had brought automobiles and trucks within the range of a vast new market and the industry began looking towards worldwide outlets for its goods. Although the cars themselves did not call for specialist vessels – though dockside handling techniques underwent a considerable change – their components – rubber, steel and so on – did; the fuel they consumed, oil and petroleum, required very special vessels. The change from coal to oil for ship propulsion made even greater demands on merchant fleets and influenced the building of bigger, more efficient tankers.

The first specialist tanker, the *Glaükauf* of 1885, was just over 2,000 tons (2,032 tonnes), but by the 1930s the bigger tankers were averaging 25,000 tons (25,400 tonnes) and oil as a raw material and as a source of energy was rapidly outstripping coal. The size of tankers at this time was largely dictated by the limitations imposed by the Suez Canal, the shortest distance between Europe and the oil fields of the Middle East; this was later to change quite dramatically for political reasons.

Opposite: A typical merchantman of the 1900s under construction at Cammell Laird. The Laird shipyard was famous for the quality of the ships it launched.

The foundry at Cammell Laird before the First World War. Standardization of parts allowed for easier construction techniques.

Merchantmen at War

The Second World War once more saw the merchant seamen in the frontline, this time even more vulnerable to U-Boat attack, in spite of the quickly introduced convoy system. Improved U-Boat and bombing techniques took a frightful toll during the first years of the war, and the entry of the Soviet Union introduced a further horror for the civilian sailor – the Soviet Arctic convoy. Added to the threat from U-Boats and Luftwaffe bombers was the dreadful weather: blinding snow, sub-zero temperatures, iced-up riggings and tempestuous seas – the life of a seaman in the freezing waters could be measured in seconds.

Convoy PQ-17

Towards the end of June 1942, the merchant skippers of PQ-17 (35 freighters crammed with tanks and planes for the Soviet Union) were huddled together in a hut at Hvalfjord in Iceland. They listened, some attentively, some indulgently, others frankly bored, to the Royal Navy briefing

The Murmansk convoys had to contend not only with the constant threat of attack from aircraft, ships and U-Boats, but also with terrible weather.

for the operation; for some of them it was the second or third time round. Few were optimistic; although they would be spared the fearful Arctic winter, they were only too aware that it would be no picnic. Not only would they have the Luftwaffe and U-Boat arm to contend with, but word had it that the 'Big Bad Wolf', the battleship *Tirpitz*, was on the prowl between them and Archangel.

On 27 June the convoy sailed from Hvalfjord to meet up with their escort to the east, six destroyers led by HMS *Keppel*, four corvettes and two anti-aircraft ships; there were also three especially equipped rescue ships, two tankers and two submarines in attendance. A covering force of four cruisers and three destroyers would accompany them for about two-thirds of the voyage. Their role would be to cope with any surface attack, leaving the escorts to deal with submarines and air attack. Minor disaster struck almost immediately: one ship ran aground on leaving harbour and another was damaged by ice in the Denmark Strait and was forced to return to Hvalfjord for repairs.

Meanwhile the *Kriegsmarine* at Kiel not only knew of PQ-17 but had drawn up an ambitious plan of attack, Operation *Rösselsprung*, a surface operation involving *Tirpitz, Hipper, Lützow*, 12 destroyers and submarines, with adequate air cover from the Luftwaffe. On 1 June Hitler gave his grudging assent, worried about endangering *Tirpitz* which he regarded as an invaluable political weapon. The operation was finally agreed in two phases.

Phase 1: *Tirpitz, Hipper* and six destroyers would move to Vestfjord; *Lützow*, six destroyers and U-Boats to Altenfjord.

Phase 2: On assurance from aerial reconnaissance that the area was clear of heavy enemy units – particularly aircraft carriers – the two groups would converge to attack the convoy in the Barents Sea.

The ice had receded far enough for the convoy to steam well north of Bear Island, further away from the Luftwaffe bases in north Norway, but on 1 July, they had been sighted by *U.253* and *U.408*. The 'Eistenfel' group of six U-Boats formed a patrol line across the convoy's line of approach; the surface force was informed.

Above: Convoy PQ-17 sails for Murmansk. Soon the ships were either scattered or sunk by enemy action.

The first attack came at 1800 hours on 2 July. Seven shore-based He 115 seaplanes made an unsuccessful torpedo attack; one He 115 was shot down and its crew was rescued by another He 115 which landed alongside the survivors. That night the convoy changed course in dense fog, hoping to shake off the shadowing reconnaissance aircraft, which it did for a while, but they were soon back. On 4 July a single He 115 dived from cloud cover and torpedoed the American freighter *Christopher Newport*, which had to be scuttled and sunk by a British submarine. By now an attack was expected by surface craft sometime during 4 July but, instead, at 2020 hours, 30 He 111s screamed out of the overcast sky and dropped their deadly 'fish' from within the convoy lines. Four were shot down, but not before three ships had been hit; two went down, the third, a Soviet tanker *Azerbaijan*, was able to steam on after putting out a fire. So far, so good, but then fate took a hand.

While the convoy was successfully resisting air attack, 1,800 miles (2,880 km) away at the Admiralty, the First Sea Lord, Sir Dudley Pound, made a fateful decision. He and his staff, convinced that the Germans would make an imminent surface attack, were left with four choices. They could turn the convoy around, in which case the Soviets would be denied valuable equipment and this would be politically unacceptable. Second, a battleship force in the area could steam toward the convoy and escort it to Archangel, leaving itself open to air attack and possible destruction; this, in turn, would allow the *Tirpitz*, the battle cruisers, pocket battleships and cruisers a clear way into the North Atlantic where they could wreak untold damage. The third

A fine painting of the P & O Rawalpindi *in her final action.*

choice was to withdraw the cruiser force and allow the convoy to proceed with a destroyer escort only. This had the merit of keeping the convoy tightly knit to fight off air and submarine attack, but left it wide open for a surface attack. In the event, Pound chose the fourth choice. He signalled the convoy to scatter – all ships were to make their way individually to Soviet ports.

The instant reaction of the escort commanders to the signal, prefixed 'most immediate', was to assume that the *Tirpitz* task force was about to attack. The convoy Commodore and his ships' masters were equally astounded as the destroyer *Keppel* raced towards them flying the signal to disperse from her masthead – 'Scatter fanwise and proceed at your utmost speed'. With naval precision the lines of merchantmen peeled off at ten degrees from

the central line of ships like the ribs of a fan, while the cruisers and destroyers headed west towards a supposedly approaching enemy. In point of fact, Adolf Hitler had again intervened and Operation *Rösselsprung* was not given the go-ahead until 5 July.

As soon as the *Kriegsmarine* realized what was happening to PQ-17, the air became alive with radio chatter; the *Tirpitz* force, much to the chagrin of Admiral Schniewind, its commander, was ordered back to base; the Luftwaffe and U-Boats were to take over. Aircraft of Wing 30 began round-the-clock bombing and torpedo attacks on the remaining 30 merchantmen, and the U-Boats went in. Ju88s screamed down and torpedoes hissed through the water. In the first 24 hours of the attack 13 freighters and a rescue ship had gone down. The following day six more were sunk. Only 11 ships of the 35 that set out from Hvalfjord reached Archangel. Of the original convoy, two had turned back, eight had been sunk by air attack, nine by U-Boats and seven which had been damaged by air attack and abandoned were later sunk by U-Boats. The Germans lost only five aircraft. A total of 430 tanks, 210 aircraft and 3,350 vehicles lay rusting at the bottom of the Barents Sea, along with 99,316 tons (100,905 tonnes) of cargo, and 153 seamen.

This was only one of the many hundreds of convoys mauled during the Second World War, their crews only able to fight back with light anti-aircraft guns and machine guns, relying for protection on their naval escorts.

Armed Merchant Cruisers

At the outbreak of the Second World War liners also went to war, either as troopships or merchant cruisers. Inadequately armed to face modern warships, they patrolled or acted on convoy escort duty.

The *Rawalpindi*

One such ship was the *Rawalpindi*, a 16,697-ton (16,964-tonne) P & O liner fitted with eight out-of-date 6-in guns, some even stamped with the crest of Queen Victoria. Stripped of her passenger fittings, designed for service in the Far East, she was sent on the Northern Patrol in the storm-tossed, icy wastes between the Faroes and Iceland.

At 1423 hours in the sub-Arctic gloom of a November afternoon Captain Kennedy sighted the *Scharnhorst*, one of the most powerful German warships afloat. Mounting nine 11-in guns and 12 5.9-in guns, she was formidable opposition for most warships afloat, especially with armour of up to 13 in (33 cm) thick.

Ordering full speed ahead, Captain Kennedy made for a fog bank on the port side, but the *Scharnhorst*, herself putting on speed, steered a course to cut off the *Rawalpindi* from the fog. As the armed merchant cruiser altered course, the German opened up with a single round of his main armament, sending up a column of water beyond the bows of the *Rawalpindi*. Sighting a cruiser on the starboard bow which was tentatively identified as 'one of ours', the old liner turned towards her, but as the silhouette became clear, Kennedy was horrified to discover it was the *Gneisenau*, sister ship to the *Scharnhorst*. Before the odds had been impossible; they were now ridiculous – so began the first surface engagement of the Second World War.

For every 6-in shell the *Rawalpindi* could get off, the Germans were replying with four 11-in. By 1511 hours, the merchant cruiser was ablaze from stem to stern. At 1558 hours a shell smashed into the forward magazine; in a sheet of flame the *Rawalpindi* split in two. Two lifeboats managed to get away and 40 men jumped into the icy water. Twenty-seven survivors were picked up by the German ships, and British warships picked up another 11. These were the only survivors out of a crew of 276.

Postwar Merchantmen

When the Second World War ended, shipowners found themselves in much the same position as after the First World War. U-Boats, bombing aircraft and mines had played havoc with the merchant fleets of the belligerent nations. Once again the first priority was to get maritime trade under way, but the attitude of the Soviet Union caused the naval planners of the West to take a close look at future naval strategy. The first type of general-purpose vessels of around 12,000 tons (12,200 tonnes) were based on the Liberty ships of the war years. These Liberty ships were built by Henry Kaiser who was a busi-

nessman rather than a shipbuilder. He reorganized a number of American shipyards to produce a standard merchant vessel. These no-nonsense ships were built to a standard tonnage, 10,500 tons (10,700 tonnes), and were spartan in the extreme with welded, instead of rivetted, prefabricated plates. The postwar ships were less spartan, but were constructed by the same

prefabricated techniques. These were at best only a stop-gap to tide shipowners over while they assessed the cargo-carrying requirements of the future, which would call for a more specialized approach to maritime trade.

Although liners became the main target of the postwar shipbuilding boom, more attention has been paid since to the development of the cargo vessel which, incidentally, has grown progressively larger as the cruise liner has grown smaller. Tankers, in particular, have grown to a mammoth size, and are the largest ships afloat. The increased size of merchant ships has brought with it many problems which influenced the design, handling and actual operation of ships.

Two general-purpose merchantmen at sea. Although merchant fleets have been reduced in size over the past few years, merchant shipping is still vital for the movement of both raw and finished products.

Tanker size was largely governed by the limitations of the Suez Canal, by far the shortest route between the oil fields of the Middle East and Western Europe, so tankers were restricted to around 25,000 tons (25,400 tonnes) and rarely, if ever, exceeded 30,000 tons (30,480 tonnes). It was the closing of the Canal after the Suez Crisis, and again after the Six Days War of 1967 that forced the development of the super tanker – this and a growing international demand for petroleum and oil-driven transport on land, sea and in the air. Faced with the closure of the Suez Canal, and a far longer route around the Cape of Good Hope, the tanker had to grow enormously in size to carry enough crude oil to make the trip a commercial proposition. This led to the birth of the VLCC (Very Large Crude Carriers), 250,000- to 275,000-ton (254,000- to 279,000-tonne) monsters that dwarfed the *Queen Elizabeth*. Once their worth had been proven, they were followed by the ULCC (Ultra Large Crude Carriers) of about 400,000 tons (406,400 tonnes), capable of carrying over 730,000 tons (742,000 tonnes) of oil. There are future plans for ships of twice this size.

Basically a tanker consists of a number of separate latitudinal compartments running the full width of the ship, filled with oil, which is usually heated to keep it thin and ensure easy unloading. They need deep water, because when fully loaded they can draw up to 75 ft (23 m), and more often than not, have to discharge their cargo at specially built tanker terminals lying off the ports.

The veteran Mk12 Racal Decca Navigator which was developed from Second World War navigators which played a major role during the Normandy Landing in 1944.

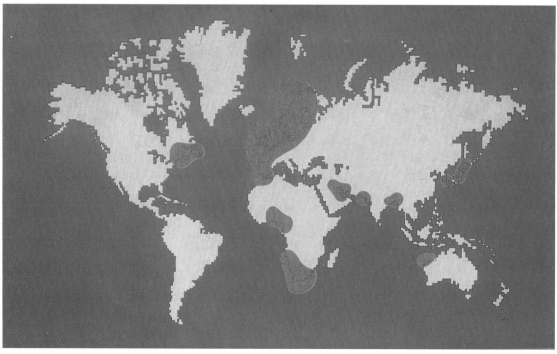

For many years, ships have been able to plot their position by Decca Navigator and Loran C.

HYPERBOLIC AIDS

Three navigational aids, Gee, Loran and Decca Navigator, have been grouped together with Consul (the Radio Direction Finding system developed by the Germans during the Second World War) under the general heading 'Hyperbolic Aids'. They are called 'hyperbolic' because the navigator, in order to use them, has to refer to special charts on which are superimposed patterns of hyperbolic lines. An hyperbola is a line which maintains a constant difference in distance from two fixed points. These systems, although differing slightly in method, are all based on the premise that radio waves from a transmitter travel in mathematical curves known as hyperbolae, in navigational terms, great circles. As these waves travel at the same speed, it is possible, by measuring the difference in time between signals received by the ship from two different stations, to plot the required curve on the chart. By repeating the process with another transmitting station in conjunction with the first two, the point of intersection is the exact position of the ship.

Gee (the British version) and Loran (the American) were being operated by the Allies as navigational aids to bombers in 1942; later they were adapted for ship navigation. The Decca Navigator was used successfully for the first time during the Allied Invasion of Europe in 1944, which called for pinpoint accuracy. In 1946 an international conference was formed to consider radio aids in navigation, at the end of which a worldwide system incorporating the four hyperbolic systems was agreed.

A gas container vessel passes through the Straits of Gibraltar. Specialist vessels have been commissioned for a number of dangerous cargoes.

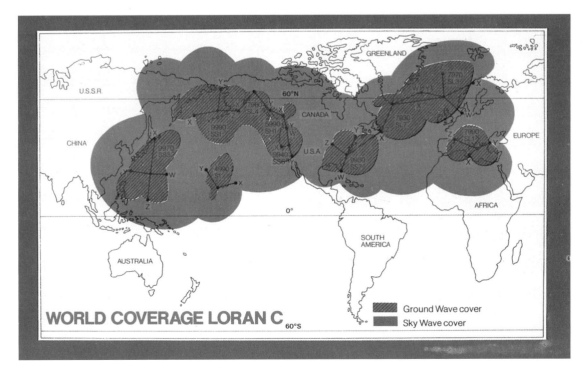

At present, about 220,000 civil marine users employ either Loran C or Decca Navigator for plotting their coastal positions.

ECHO-SOUNDING TECHNIQUES

Modern echo-sounding devices owe a lot to an Anglo-French echo-sounding device invented at the end of the First World War known as ASDIC. The Allied Submarine Detection Investigation Committee was set up to devise a means of locating submarines operating below the surface – both countries were very conscious of just how close the German U-Boat *guerre de course* had come to succeeding. The result of their search was ASDIC. The same method, albeit far more sophisticated, is still in use today. Renamed Sonar – SOund NAvigation and Ranging – its use as a depth-gauge aid is of equal importance as its role in submarine detection. It has also been adapted for detecting mines, and the fishing industry uses it for locating shoals of fish. Technically it works as follows. A transducer, using the vibrating properties of quartz, emits a high frequency sound-wave which, passing through the water, is reflected back by any solid object it encounters. As sound travels at a known speed through water, the depth of an object or the sea bed can be calculated from the interval of time it takes the sound to travel from the bottom of the ship to the sea bed and back to the receiver. In the case of a moving object, a submarine or a shoal of fish, a bearing can be obtained by observing the Doppler effect, or change of note.

Opposite: The modern trawler is armed with a complex suite of electronics to help in the hunt for fish.

A trawler skipper uses the latest Racal Decca sonar and radar to place him among the fish.

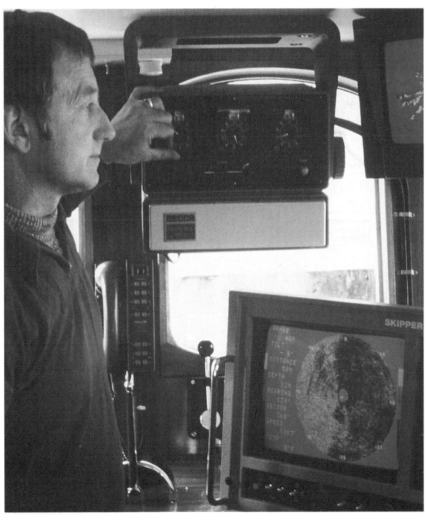

The OCL container ship Tor Bay. *Containerization means that ships have to spend far less time in port.*

The Future

Looking to the future of both passenger and cargo-carrying ships, the development of the hovercraft and hydrofoil hold considerable possibilities. A hovercraft rides on a cushion of pressurized air between it and the water over which it is travelling and is held steady by thick rubber 'skirts'. High speeds, between 55 and 65 knots, can be obtained from powerful jet engines as there is little water resistance and it is driven forward by propellers. Unfortunately at the moment there is one serious drawback that has yet to be overcome: hovercraft are unable to operate in very stormy or rough weather, as they can easily be blown off course. This makes them a rather temperamental short-haul vessel, but since the introduction of the SRN-4 in 1968, great strides have been made in its development. Already 165-ton (168-

tonne) hovercraft can carry 610 passengers or 256 passengers and 30 cars, but there are still a number of design problems to solve.

In a manner similar to the hovercraft, the hydrofoil lifts its hull out of the water and skids across the surface on foils. This was first tried out on Lake Maggiore in Italy in 1906, but the idea was not introduced commercially until 1956 as a fast ferry service between Sicily and Italy. Although the high rate of fuel consumption limits them to short journeys, the naval architects are already considering the possibilities of adapting the system to ocean liners with speeds of at least 60 knots and over.

The growth of containerization has also had a remarkable influence on the development of cargo ships. Time spent by a ship in harbour is money wasted, and it is far cheaper to load goods into containers at factories and depots than at the dockside, and naval architects now design ships to take standard-size containers, both in the hold and as deck cargo. By this means expensive 'turnaround' time is cut to a minimum and it also allows a ship to handle any number of different cargoes at the same time, from transister radios to washing machines. Some of these ships can carry up to 2,300 standard containers, a total cargo weight of about 34,000 tons (34,500 tonnes).

To speed up loading and unloading even further, Roll-on/Roll-off ships have been introduced – Ro-Ro for short. Cargo is loaded by means of heavy-duty forklift trucks from a ramp in the stern; cars and heavy mechanical vehicles can be driven straight into the hold. Other specialist ships are developed almost daily: Liquified Natural Gas Container ships that are able to keep the gas at the correct pressure and very necessary low temperatures, car ferries, cargo liners and bulk cargo vessels.

Soviet hydrofoils operating in the Black Sea port of Odessa. Large-scale surface-effect vessels could well become important in merchant-shipping terms.

WEAPONRY

Painted in 1895, the battleship USS Maine entered service during the American Civil War in 1865.

For more than five hundred years the gun ruled supreme as the most effective weapon in naval warfare, from its introduction as a 'man killer' to repel boarders, to 'ship smashers' which culminated in the massive 18-in guns of the *Yamato* and *Musashi*.

Even up to Trafalgar sea battles had to be fought at point-blank range; ships virtually had to be alongside each other for shot to have any appreciable effect on the heavy wooden walls – first-raters of Nelson's time had hulls of 18-in (46-cm) thick oak. In

HMS Thunderer, launched in 1872, was modernized in the 1890s. Here, after her refit, she steams past an old training 'ship-of-the-line' in Portsmouth Harbour.

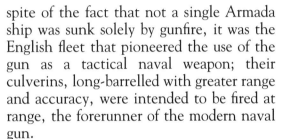

spite of the fact that not a single Armada ship was sunk solely by gunfire, it was the English fleet that pioneered the use of the gun as a tactical naval weapon; their culverins, long-barrelled with greater range and accuracy, were intended to be fired at range, the forerunner of the modern naval gun.

Throughout its history the naval gun has been either loaded from the muzzle or through a breech, and it was not until the last quarter of the 19th century that the breech-loaded gun became standard. The early breech-loaders were built up of wrought-iron staves and hoops that were welded together and fitted with a detachable powder chamber. The muzzle-loaders, on the other hand, were cast in a single piece in bronze or iron from a clay mould. The difference between the guns used by the Elizabethans and those of Nelson was one of refinement and size; no fundamental change took place until the coming of the shell gun and iron cladding.

The transition from muzzle-loading to breech-loading was inevitable, although many navies clung to the former method until the early 1870s. From then progress was rapid and by the 1890s the pattern had been set for the modern naval gun. Although breech guns had been designed as early as 1846, it was not until William Armstrong came along that ordnance became an exact science, rather than handed down by rule of thumb; before Armstrong there was very little knowledge of the magnitude of the forces being

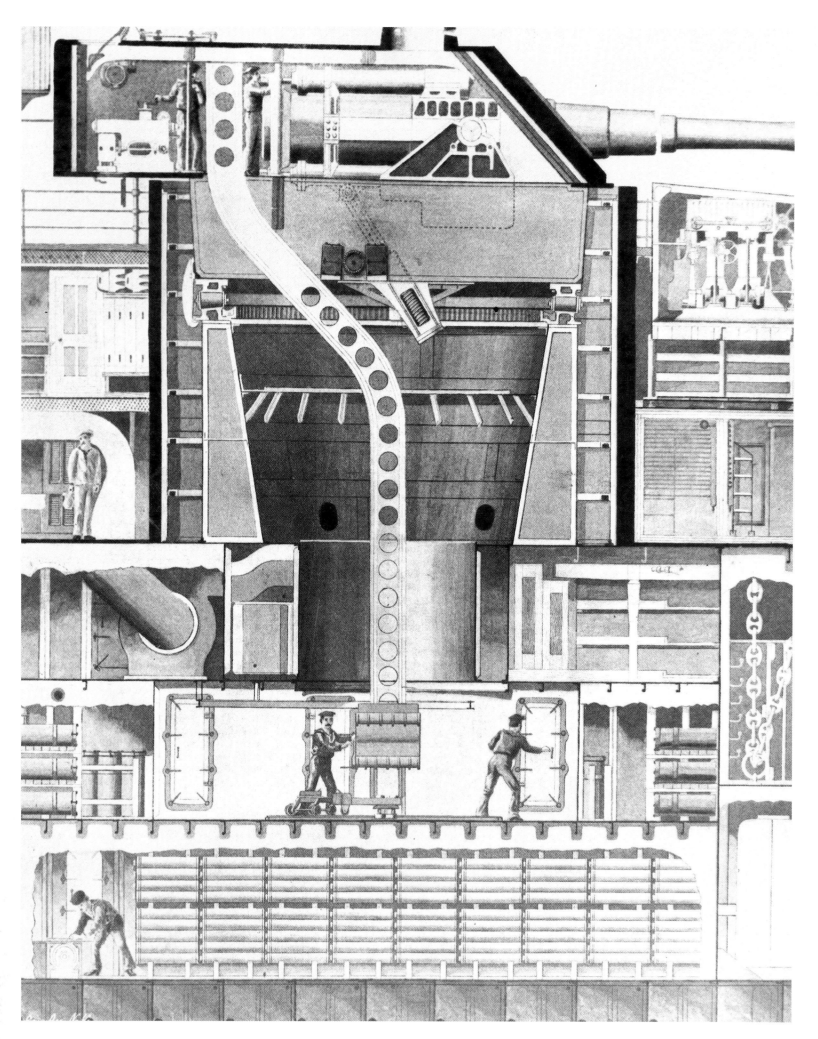

exerted in the gun chamber and barrel. Another deciding factor in turning to a breech-loading system was 'windage', the necessary space between the shell and the bore of the gun to allow loading from the muzzle; this to a great extent negated the advantage gained from rifling. Already gunmakers had learned a lesson from the infantryman's rifled musket that could project a bullet further and with greater accuracy; various systems of rifling were being applied to naval ordnance.

Based on sound engineering principles, Armstrong's guns took into account the pressures generated by the force of an explosive charge and were constructed accordingly. Abandoning the principle of a single iron tube he made up his gun of a number of tubes, or 'hoops', of wrought iron, shrunk one upon the other, giving tension to the inner tube. Guns grew enormously in size and weight. By 1860 the largest 10-in smooth bore had grown to a 13-in gun weighing 22 tons (tonnes), delivering a shell of 600 lb (273 kg); rifled breech-loaders from 6.3 in to 12.5 in in calibre. Yet until the advent of the armour-piercing shell these projectiles were unable to pierce the iron cladding now being added to warships. The wooden truck mounting gave way to wrought-iron slide mountings fitted with compression systems to absorb the increased recoil. In 1862 a further advancement took place in naval gunnery when the coastal defence vessel, the *Prince Albert*, was designed to carry four centre-line revolving turrets – modern battleship gun-mounting was beginning to take place. At first these turrets were turned manually by rack-and-pinion gear, a slow tedious process that took over a minute to complete one full revolution. In early turret ships, guns not only had to be loaded at one elevation, they also had to be trained down the centre-line each time a shell and charge was rammed home. Valuable time was wasted cranking the guns back to the desired angle of fire for each salvo, so much so that for a period during the 1880s some navies rejected turrets entirely, reverting to fixed barbettes. Gunnery officers clamoured for faster, more accurate firing control and gunmakers and the ordnance designers of the maritime nations worked feverishly to be first in the field with new efficient systems.

By the mid-1890s most of the teething problems had been overcome and the gun that emerged was to remain standard, subject only to improvement in detail and degree; the fundamental system has remained pretty much the same. The use of powerful electric motors enabled turret guns to be loaded at any elevation, but the Americans found the mechanical systems too complicated and preferred to use their electrical power to drive the guns into and out of the firing elevation before and after loading and reload in an horizontal position. In the Second World War this happened smoothly on the gun's recoil, and re-elevated as the gun ran out for the next salvo.

While these vast technical developments were going on, one aspect of naval gunnery had hardly changed since the time of Drake – the aiming of the gun. In those days the cannon would be elevated through 20 degrees by means of a quoin and trained on the target with a training lever; hitting the enemy rested entirely on the skill of the gunner. Until the beginning of the 20th century, accuracy depended entirely on the skill of the gunlayer, a breed born, not made.

Even by the early 1890s the usual method of aiming the gun was the 'tangent sight', a simple method using a foresight and backsight, as in a small arms musket. A metal rod attached to the muzzle of the gun acted as the foresight and an octagonal rear sight alongside the breech, notched at the top and scaled with ranges, could be moved into the vertical position by the gunlayer, according to the type of shot to be fired. To register hits on a rolling gun platform depended entirely on the skill of the gunlayer and as these were in short supply, more mechanical means were sought to lay shells accurately on target. Some were practical, others not, but none was very successful. Among the more fanciful was this highly involved system; 'Let two observers, each visible from the other, take their stations at the end of a rope whose length is accurately measured, and simultaneously measure the angle between the other observer and the target, the three angles and one side of a triangle are thus obtained, and the side wanted can be readily calculated. Take for instance one observer at the main top mast cross-trees, and the other in the main chains, the main topmast backstay will answer for a base' – and this in the heat of battle on a heaving deck with shell crashing into the ship. A simpler method

An artist's impression of a vertical section through an American battleship of 1905, showing the magazines, barbette and turret.

was to allow the enemy to fire first, count the seconds from the flash and multiply by 1,100 to obtain the range in feet, but this always assumed that his initial salvoes would not arrive on target.

A range finder that could be operated by one man was introduced in 1892, the first of many ideas to be tried out over the next few years. This consisted of two mirrors, one fixed, the other moveable. The observer, looking into two eyepieces, had an image of the target (which passed to the eye through prisms in the fixed mirror) and by adjusting the moveable mirror, which carried an image, until the two fused into one, he was able to read the image off a scale. Later, one of the images was inverted and the observer lined up the two topmasts of the target ship, to read off the range. The Germans followed with a range finder based on a stereoscopic principle in which the observer could see a series of numbers passing across a magnified image of the target, which sharpened up in focus at the correct range. This system, much faster than the split-image one as the observer was not required to manipulate anything, did, however, have one serious drawback: the observer was required to have stereoscopic vision, and many people do not have such vision.

Despite the introduction of range finders, gunnery was far from an exact science. What was needed was a method of directing the guns.

Direction Finding

With the coming of *Dreadnought*, a single-calibre ship, which implied co-ordinated firing of all guns, some method was sought to control the gunnery from one point. The Japanese had shown at Tsushima that good results could be obtained at 7,000 yd (6,400 m) and above by an officer behind a range finder, transmitting a range to his gunners, which could be corrected by observers in the tops 'spotting' the splashes and correcting the range; but was it necessary for any aiming to be done by the guns? The Royal Navy reasoned that still better results could be obtained by controlling the whole of a ship's main armament from a point high on the foremast, away from the smoke and noise of the gun turret. In 1912 the R.N. introduced a 'director system', in which a gunnery officer controlled the ship's main armament, transmitting the necessary elevation and angle of train automatically to the guns. He then fired a broadside electronically by depressing a key. This system arrived just in time for the First World War.

The German Navy had a more simple

The first shots are fired by the Japanese main squadron during the war of 1904–5 against the Russian Fleet.

Opposite top: A Barr and Stroud 26-ft (8-m) duplex range finder on an anti-vibration mounting for naval use. This was manned by two ratings.

Opposite bottom: Incorporating three electro-optic sensors, a television, a thermal imaging camera and a laser range finder, the Sea Archer 30 electro-optical director is still light enough to be mounted high in a ship's superstructure.

Framed by a Mk 12/22 fire control radar and SG (small) and SC (large) radar, a gunnery trainer peers out of USS Ault's Mk 37 gun director in 1945.

A Thomson CSF TAVITAC computerized action and information centre aboard a modern French warship.

RADAR AND RADIO DIRECTION FINDING

The beginning for the Second World War saw the introduction of a position-finding, collision-avoiding, detection device that was to have far-reaching effects not only in naval warfare but in the art of navigation. 'Radar', an abbreviation for RAdio Direction And Ranging, is a method of detecting the bearing of objects and any other ships or aircraft by sending out pulses of radio waves. Working on the same principle as sonar, the time taken for a pulse of very short wavelength to bounce back from an object can be measured in a cathode-ray tube. As the speed of radio waves is known, this time can be automatically translated into distance. Whereas the speed of sound through water is approximately 5,000 ft (1,500 m) per second, the speed of radio waves through the atmosphere is that of light, about 186,000 miles (299,000 km) per

second. This, of course, means that the cathode-ray tube must be a particularly sensitive and accurate measuring instrument, but also allows the plotting of the fastest aircraft or missile. A transmitting aerial, sending out a narrow radio beam, 'scanning' through 360 degrees about the ship, is synchronized with a revolving light 'trace' on the cathode-ray tube; any object encountered brightens the trace at a point from the centre of the tube equivalent to its distance and bearing. The range of a radar set is controlled by its height above the sea, but in big ships the range is never less than 25 miles (40 km). As in the case of light, the very short radio waves travel in a straight line and cannot bend around corners, which, because of the curvature of the earth's surface, more or less cuts down radar range to horizon distance. However, this 'failing' can be considerably increased by working in conjunction with radar-equipped aircraft.

Even before radar, radio directions could be transmitted from ship and shore to establish a bearing, and are still helpful navigational aids, especially when beyond visual and radar range of land. A radio beam or beacon can be located and a bearing or fix taken by means of a radio direction-finding set or D/F set. The principle is the same as that used in a portable radio set – a loop aerial, which, if rotated, will either increase or decrease the volume of sound. When the loop of a D/F set is trained at right angles to the transmitting station, a 'null' or loss of sound occurs. This is done because the minimum signal can be detected more accurately than the maximum signal which occurs when the full plane of the loop aerial faces the transmitter. The correct bearing is, therefore, at right angles to the rotating loop at a point when the 'null' occurs. Radio beacons transmit regular signals on fixed frequencies, each of which can be recognized by its individual frequency and type of signal. This often allows navigators to obtain two or more cross bearings, making for greater accuracy.

To assist their U-Boat packs to navigate across the Atlantic Ocean and North Sea, the Germans introduced 'Consul'. Originally known to the Germans as *'Sonne'*, or sun, a Consul station sent out a pattern of signals radiating at 15-degree intervals like rays from the sun. Although the principle of Consul was complex, it was a simple method to use – the only equipment needed was an ordinary radio receiver. Radio waves in the form of dots are transmitted into one sector, and in the form of dashes in the section adjacent to it. By using a D/F loop to obtain a bearing, the navigator was able to determine in which of the 15-degree sectors his U-Boat was situated. He listened for a continuous note to fade, then counted the dots or dashes which followed – this told him if he were in a 'dot sector' or 'dash sector' – until they too faded. Then, by reference to a special table, he translated the 'count' into the 'Great Circle' bearing of the U-Boat. However, this was in some ways a two-edged weapon for not only were the Luftwaffe able to use it but so too were the R.A.F.

High above a Royal Navy ship is the giant frame of its surveillance radar. The problem that faces many navies is the lack of range that ship-mounted radars give against air attack. Following the Falklands War, the Royal Navy has brought into service a helicopter-mounted radar.

system. Although it used a central 'director' system, it was left to the individual turret to pick up the target and fire individually on the roll. The argument, director versus turret-fire, was to last for years, but once the conditions deteriorated at Jutland – the targets, obscured by spray, shell splashes and smoke – the British gunnery proved more effective; their losses came from badly designed battle-cruisers and, as Admiral Hipper summed up after the battle, 'That the English did not achieve more was due to their inadequate shells'.

Salvo firing is at best imprecise, the shells falling in a pattern around a target, the centre of which is the point of aim. The gunnery control officer adjusts his aim as the shells 'straddle' the target, splashes appearing simultaneously on either side – hits, curiously enough, are difficult to see, as most of the armour-piercing shells explode within the ship. Once he has straddled the target, the gunnery control officer can adjust the range to register 'hits', but this has to be constantly altered and hits are a matter of statistics based on the number of shells fired. However, at Jutland the Germans demonstrated that 'ladder' firing was a superior and quicker method of obtaining an accurate range. Instead of waiting to read the splashes, their gunners fired a number of salvoes each side of the estimated range – a 'ladder' which allowed for rapid calibration.

Director sighting brought a new accuracy to naval gunnery which was only superseded by the introduction of radar with its ability to plot ranges far more accurately than a range finder, particularly in murk and fog, or at night. Prior to the introduction of radar, it was hoped, between the wars, that aircraft spotting would solve the problem of long-range ship-to-ship engagements out of sight of the enemy, and one important function of the aircraft carrier was to control the air above a battle to allow the spotters to work unhindered. In fact this was rarely used during the Second World War, as aircraft became major attack weapons in their own right.

Penetration and damage, proportional to the calibre of the shell, rise rapidly with the velocity of impact. Another of the many lessons learned from Tsushima was that the 10-in shell was in no way as effective as the 12-in shell, and thus the latter, thereafter, became the minimum calibre for a battleship's main armament, though the Germans clung to 11 in even for their Second World War pocket-battleships. Some thought had been given to using smaller calibre shells fired at a higher velocity, but this had one serious fault. Shells with a higher muzzle velocity cause greater wear on the gun barrel which shortens the accurate life of the gun and calls for regunning, a major operation that can only be carried out at a well-equipped port. Hence, it is essential for battles fought far from home and major ports that guns last the duration of the fight. This led to the introduction of heavier shells with a lower velocity and consequently less wear, 13.5 in, 15 in and eventually 16 in and the massive 18 in of the Japanese, though the latter hardly had the opportunity to prove their worth. So shells went up in calibre and weight and down in muzzle velocity, and the weight of broadside delivered became all important.

Anti-aircraft Defence

The advocates of the big gun and the battleship were not totally unaware of the danger from air attack. Although they refused to believe that a battleship could be sunk by bombing, they realized that it could well be damaged, and they gave some thought to anti-aircraft defence. Lack of

Opposite: An American sailor polishes the breech of a gun aboard a battleship, somewhere in the Pacific, before battle during the Second World War.

A pair of Italian Oto Melara 76/62 compact gun mounts. These dual-role anti-ship anti-aircraft guns have an automatic rate of fire of 85 rounds/minute.

space aboardship precluded the introduction of 'high angle' guns solely for air defence – the *Bismarck*, for instance, had only 16 3-in specialist AA guns and the *Hood* had none at all – so secondary armament had to serve a twin purpose, never a wholly successful compromise. For normal surface action, 4-in and 5-in guns could be elevated up to 20 degrees and beyond that to 85 degrees for anti-aircraft defence. By and large, warships relied on smaller calibre AA guns of 40 mm and 20 mm and heavy machine guns, pumping the sky full of metal on the assumption that by the law of averages an aircraft must fly into some flak.

With the development of missiles in modern naval warfare, the days of the big gun have passed to be replaced by small calibre, 4-in, fully automatic, computer-controlled guns of great accuracy. Such guns were used to great effect in shore bombardment during the Falklands Campaign.

The Torpedo

Until the air-flight missile, the torpedo did more to transform naval warfare than even the aerial bomb. The torpedo, a guided missile moving at a set depth, is still the general attack weapon used by conventional submarines and the primary weapon fired from surface or air against them.

There were many attempts to design a torpedo – but the form it took, the one we know today, was the work of Robert Whitehead, the English manager of a Fiume engineering works. His 'locomotive' torpedo was evolved from a clockwork-driven craft fitted with an explosive charge, invented in 1865 by an Austrian artillery man, Captain Lupis. This crude affair, guided to its target by lines attached to its rudder, led Whitehead to produce a cigar-shaped 'fish', propelled by compressed air, which could travel submerged for 220 yd (100 m) at 6 knots.

In 1871 the Royal Navy bought the rights and began experimenting in firing the torpedo from HMS *Vesuvius*; it was not until six years later that the first specially designed 'torpedo boat', HMS *Lightning* put in an appearance. The world's navies immediately saw the potential in a cheaply built craft capable of sinking the biggest battleship, and the race was on to build small fast boats. In practice the torpedo was too erratic to be much of a menace, its propulsion unit too fragile, its firing mechanism too temperamental. Still its threat was sufficient to deter ships from engaging in the close blockade of an enemy coast.

A Marconi Tigerfish torpedo, before leaving the factory. The cable at the rear is connected to the submarine's torpedo fire-control computer during the inital attack. As it nears the target, its own onboard computer takes over for the final attack.

As the torpedo became more reliable, Whitehead introduced his 'secret', a hydrostatic disc working against a spring, with a pendulum and linkage to horizontal rudders to give depth control. A more efficient launching platform was sought, one that itself would also be able to sink attacking torpedo boats. The 'torpedo boat destroyer', later cut to 'destroyer', was an immediate success. Larger and faster than a torpedo boat, it carried a 12-pounder and two 6-pounder guns. The first of these sleek, sinister-looking 'torpedo boat destroyers', the *Havock*, appeared with a 'turtle-back' forecastle, displaced 240 tons (244 tonnes) and had a remarkable speed of 27.6 knots.

By now the Whitehead torpedo was regarded as a very dangerous weapon indeed; 14 in (36 cm) in diameter, it could travel submerged for 1,000 yd (914 m) at a speed of 25 knots and carried a 33-lb (15-kg) explosive warhead. The cigar shape, on the advice of hydrodynamic experts, had given way to a blunt nose with a pistol detonator. At the turn of the century, the introduction of 'heaters' extended the torpedo's range to 2,000 yd (1,830 m) and its diameter had risen to

18 in (46 cm), then went up to 21 in (53 cm), resulting in bigger, more destructive warheads – gyros had also been fitted to keep the 'fish' on course.

Already a deadly weapon, it became even more deadly when the submarine became a practical proposition. Now a torpedo could be delivered from below the surface, silent and unseen, but for a telltale trail of air bubbles below the surface. It became the main weapon of the German U-Boat arm in the First World War, a fearful weapon up to 22 ft (6.7 m) long with a range of 3,750 yd (3,430 m) at 44 knots or 10,000 yd (9,140 m) at 28 knots.

The basic design of the torpedo remained the same between the wars, but great effort was made to improve its performance. The British experimented with, then abandoned, the idea of liquid oxygen, 'enriched air', as a propellant on the grounds of danger and risk, preferring to develop the Brotherhood cycle engine. The Japanese, having no such qualms, persevered with liquid oxygen and came up with the monstrous 'Long Lance', which was later to be used as a suicide weapon. This giant torpedo, 24 in (61 cm) in diameter, could travel 25,000 yd (23,000 m) at a maximum speed of 49 knots, as opposed to the standard 21-in (53-cm) with a range of 7,000-10,000 yd (6,400-9.140 m) at a speed of 45 and 30 knots respectively.

During the Second World War the Germans introduced the first workable electric-drive torpedo which after initial teething problems could deliver its warhead without the give-away trail of bubbles. An acoustic homing warhead was also produced, but the magnetic fusing system proved highly unreliable, much to the relief of the Allies.

The Americans made a significant contribution to the development of the torpedo when, in 1943, they came out with a lightweight acoustic anti-submarine torpedo which would be dropped from an aircraft. This was developed after the war, when torpedoes were divided into 'heavyweight', for firing from submarines and 'lightweight' for firing from helicopters, fast patrol boats and surface warships. These at first passively homed in on the noise emitted from a submarine's engines, but by the 1950s, the actively motivated Mk 43, 44 and 46 torpedoes were being exploited to become the standard lightweight torpedoes of the NATO countries by the 1970s. Another development was the British Mk 23, a wire-guided dual-purpose anti-ship and anti-submarine weapon.

The heavyweight Mk 24 Tigerfish, a more advanced weapon, has now replaced the standard torpedoes, and the Stingray has replaced the American Mk 44 and 46. The Stingray, the most up-to-date lightweight torpedo, came into service in 1983, and was the first of a new generation of computer-based autonomous homing torpedoes, capable of being dropped by parachute from a helicopter and able to out-think and take out the most advanced submarine. The latest in this line of computerized torpedoes, the Spearfish, has yet to come into service, but it is already predicted that it will outstrip any other torpedo in service, an effective counter-weapon to any foreseeable submarine threat.

Scicon's concept of an unmanned computerized submarine of the early 21st century. One of its main roles would be to track enemy submarines. It could either release torpedoes or accelerate to high speed and destroy itself and the enemy submarine.

Mines

A passive, nevertheless effective, form of defence is the naval mine. The Russians were the first to use mines as we know them today, when they sowed them around the Crimea during the war of 1854-56. M. Jacobi's invention was mechanically fired by means of a chemical fuse of sulphuric acid in a glass tube, but the amount of explosive used was insufficient to cause any lasting damage to a capital ship.

International law demanded that mines should be moored and have a fail-safe mechanism which rendered them harmless should they break adrift. They were of two main types: 'observation' or 'controlled' mines that could be detonated electronically from the shore, and 'contact' mines that exploded when struck by a ship. A number of methods were tried to detonate the latter, but until the later stages of the First World War, this consisted of crushing one of a number of soft lead 'horns'. Before the end of the war, the British were experimenting with mines that were set off by the magnetic field of a ship passing over them. Although slow into the field, the British introduced their mine, the H.2, in 1916 to great effect; 25 per cent of the U-Boat losses were caused by mines.

Mines were used far more widely and with even better results during the Second World War, the conventional 'contact' ones being supplemented by magnetic and acoustic mines. Laid by surface vessels, submarines or aircraft, these mines could either be moored or scattered on the sea bed in relatively shallow water. In really shallow water, mines were designed to be activated by the pressure wave of surface ships and were practically unsweepable. Minesweeping became a very necessary, if hazardous, operation, carried out by either vessels specially designed for the job, or fishing trawlers adapted for the purpose. Wooden trawlers were particularly useful in sweeping magnetic mines, since a steel-hulled vessel would herself be liable to explode them; later fibreglass hulls were used.

Conventional mines could be swept and exploded on the surface by means of a heavy wire towed between two minesweepers. In some cases a paravane, a torpedo-shaped underwater device with serrated teeth in its forward end, was towed on a wire from the bows of a ship. The mine's moorings were cut and once the mine bobbed to the surface it would be harmlessly despatched by rifle fire. Acoustic mines were destroyed by simulating the noise of a ship's propeller over them. Pressure mines were the most difficult to sweep; they had to be first detected by sonar, then frogmen sent down to remove them.

Today the nautical mine offers an ever-growing threat in naval warfare, as localized 'brush fires' have clearly demonstrated. The modern mine, complex and easily laid, consequently diminishing the effectiveness of traditional sweeping, has brought about entirely new methods of detection. Mine hunting, detection and recognition of type, is now carried out by sensitive sonar equipment, either towed or mounted in the hulls of minesweepers. Although able to detect and categorize deep-sea mines, the hunt can be only as fast as the ship itself, and in modern naval warfare speed is of the essence. The answer is to search from a helicopter-towed system

Opposite: The crew of a Second World War German minesweeper prepare to lower a minesweeping sledge while on operations in the Mediterranean.

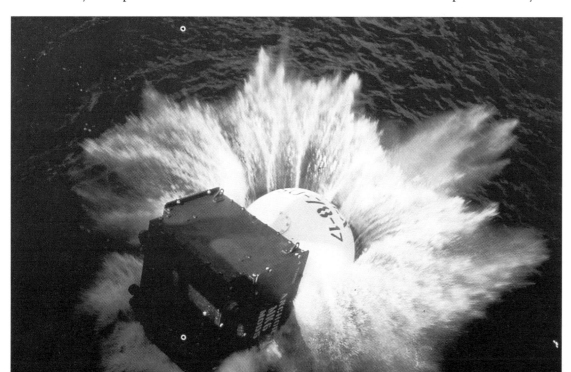

A modern American mine is laid. The current generation of mines can be programmed to activate themselves when certain types of vessel are in the area but will let others pass.

which allows the bed of the sea to be covered at the speed of the aircraft.

An underwater vehicle, towed by an electro-mechanical cable, feeds information to a display consol housed in the helicopter. About 10 ft (3 m) long, the vehicle carries side-searching multi-beam sonar that rapidly searches the sea bed for mines. By this method, mines can be detected, classified for type and recorded for later destruction.

Depth-charges

Another weapon first introduced in 1916, the depth-charge has proved over the years to be the singular most successful weapon against submarines and although today's depth-charges are far more sophisticated than their First World War counterparts, the general concept remains the same. It is basically a canister filled with high explosive, set to explode at a given depth. This is done by means of a hydrostatically controlled valve, operated by the pressure of the water against a spring, the tension of which can be varied to correspond to the depth at which the depth-charge is re-

quired to explode; a piston then detonates it.

At first, depth-charges were rolled from the stern of warships, but later were fired from a depth-charge thrower; in both instances the ship had to pass over the submarine before it could deliver its attack. Prior to the depth-charge thrower, a number of other projectors had been tried; one of these was the 7.5-in howitzer which fired a spherical bomb weighing 200 lb (91 kg). As it only weighed 35 cwt (1,780 kg) it was small enough to be carried aboard trawlers and minesweepers, but inherent weaknesses curtailed its use. An even more dangerous weapon to use was the 11-in breech-loading howitzer, which could fire a 350-lb (160-kg) shell nearly 3,000 yd (2,740 m); this was only really effective against submarines that had surfaced. Both weapons were hit and miss as difficulty was experienced in exploding the bomb or shell at a given depth. This difficulty was removed with the coming of the depth-charge, which, once a submarine's depth had been estimated, could be set to detonate near her, causing lethal

A Soviet 'Petya' class frigate. It is fitted with a pair of RBU 6000 12-barrel anti-submarine rockets. It also carries AS torpedoes and depth-charges. This ship has been on extended patrol as can be seen from the peeling paintwork. Soviet ships take a new number depending on the task force to which they are assigned.

damage, especially if it exploded below the vessel.

Submariners feared depth-charge attacks far more than any other form of attack. Trapped in their iron box, fathoms below the surface, they could clearly hear the increasing thud of the enemy's engines as he came in to attack. In the silence that followed they would count the seconds until the fearful explosion that sent them sprawling about the boat. If they were lucky, if their attacker had misread the depth, the boat would heave convulsively,

the glass of gauges shatter, the lights go out and fine jets of water force their way through sprung plates, which could be quickly staunched. If, however, the attacker guessed correctly and the depth-charge exploded just under the boat, the result was horrendous. Plates would buckle, water rush into the boat, and in pitch darkness the panic-stricken crew would struggle helplessly against the inrushing sea in a desperate attempt to get out. Little wonder some unfortunate submariners lost their reason during a depth-charge attack.

The underwater blast of an Asroc nuclear missile is watched from a distance by the crew of USS Agerholm.

Although the conventional depth-charge thrower remained the standard projector throughout the Second World War, towards the end, new improved methods were introduced which have since been developed: the Squid and Limbo, the aerial depth-charge and the Hedgehog. These allowed an attack to be made before the position of the submarine was reached. The Squid, and subsequently the Limbo, an improved version, were three-barrelled spigot mortars capable of firing full-sized depth-charges ahead of the ship, eliminating the need for an escort to pass over a target before an attack. The Limbo had the added advantage of being able to set the depth of the explosion directly from the sonar plot. During this same period the Americans developed an aircraft depth-charge fitted with bomb fins for greater accuracy in flight, pre-set to explode at 30 ft (9 m), for use against diving U-Boats caught on the surface.

The Hedgehog, an elaborate weapon used with devastating effect, consisted of an ahead-firing spigot mortar which discharged 24 small contact-fused bombs. This could be fired while the U-Boat was still held in the forward-probing Asdic beam, and produced a very effective elliptical spread of bombs that gave the maximum chance for a submarine 'kill'. Modern developments include the introduction of an active homing device to steer the depth-charge to the vicinity of the target before it explodes. Dropped from helicopters, these depth-charges have proved highly effective in action; it was these that caused so much damage to the Argentinian submarine *Santa Fe* that she sank at South Georgia during the Falklands Campaign. A nuclear explosive to widen the 'kill' area of a depth-charge has also been developed, but results have not been revealed.

An early example of a
Regulus nuclear cruise
missile is fired in the mid-
1950s. The problem with
this missile was that the
submarine had to surface to
fire it. The Regulus was very
inaccurate and its
development was cancelled in
favour of ballistic missiles.

Missile Warfare

As early as 1937 the United States was experimenting with guided weapons, 'drone' vehicles launched from ships to take out hostile aircraft and sink enemy ships, but it was the results obtained by German rocket scientists during the Second World War that really triggered the research into missiles.

Before the war had ended the United States Navy was investigating the use of guided missiles to be used in surface-to-air and surface-to-surface roles, particularly in view of the Japanese massed attacks and kamikaze techniques, and although this inspired the 'Lark' programme, nothing of consequence materialized before the end of the war. In 1948/49 the American submarines *Carbonero* and *Cusk* were adapted to take the 'Loon' missile system, an improved version of the German 'doodlebug' VI rocket, which was launched from a catapult abaft the bridge. This led to the Regulus I missile, a far different proposition and the first of today's modern missiles. Regulus I, housed in two cylindrical hangars aboard the submarines *Tunny* and *Barbero*, was an air-breathing 32-ft (10-m) long anti-ship missile with a range of 500 miles (800 km). The Regulus II which soon followed was all of 57 ft (17 m) long and demanded large, specially built submarines to house it. Two were built, the *Grayback* and *Growler* and, in 1956, the nuclear-powered *Halibut*, but the life of Regulus II was short; after only five years it was taken out of service. The Soviets also had claimed their share of German rocket scientists and technicians and, at the end of the war, were not slow in following the American lead. In 1961 they converted 12 of their submarines into missile-carrying vessels, along the lines of the *Tunny* and *Barbero*, armed with Shaddock missiles. These 40-ft (12-m) long missiles, travelling at the speed of sound, were able to deliver a nuclear- or high-explosive warhead a maximum distance of 520 miles (832 km).

A race was on between the Soviet Union and the West to produce ship-launched missiles that travelled further, faster and offered the maximum amount of destructive power. With the decline of the big gun and the demise of the battleship and battlecruiser as capital ships, the world's navies turned to building smaller warships, which, however, had a greater hitting power. The missiles they carried fell into three categories: surface-to-air (SAM), surface-to-surface (SSM) and anti-submarine warfare (ASW); all had to be small enough to be carried in fast attack craft. The improvement in radar tracking has not only produced highly complex and efficient attack systems, but has bred a generation of defence missiles to counter them; thus, in theory, Exocet air-to-surface or surface-to-surface missiles can be taken out by a Sea Wolf. The use of missiles during the Falklands Campaign underlined that they still had teething problems, but by the end of the confrontation many of these had been resolved.

Missiles Commonly Used at Sea

AS.12 (France)

An air-to-surface missile used mainly as an anti-fast-patrol-boat weapon, it is usually fired from a helicopter. Wire-guided, this spin-stabilized missile is steered to its target by the operator manipulating a control stick.
Warhead: 62.2 lb (28.3 kg) high explosive; length: 6 ft 1 in (1.85 m); weight: 170 lb (77.3 kg); range: about 20,000 ft (6,100 m); speed: 230 mph (370 km/h).
A variation of this is the AS.15 which has a cruising speed of more than 600 mph (960 km/h).

Exocet (France)

This medium-range surface-to-surface or air-to-surface missile proved its worth in the Falklands; flying very low it is guided to its target by a radar-homing head. One of the most formidable naval weapons ever produced, it carries a highly destructive warhead of 352 lb (160 kg) of high explosive, and can travel at almost the speed of sound over a distance of 40 miles (64 km).

Ikara (Australia)

Developed in Australia, this long-range anti-submarine weapon is an all-weather rocket-propelled missile which can be homed to its target from a distance of 11 miles (18 km). The Ikara is launched from shipboard, and on reaching the target position, drops a homing torpedo by parachute, which automatically disengages on

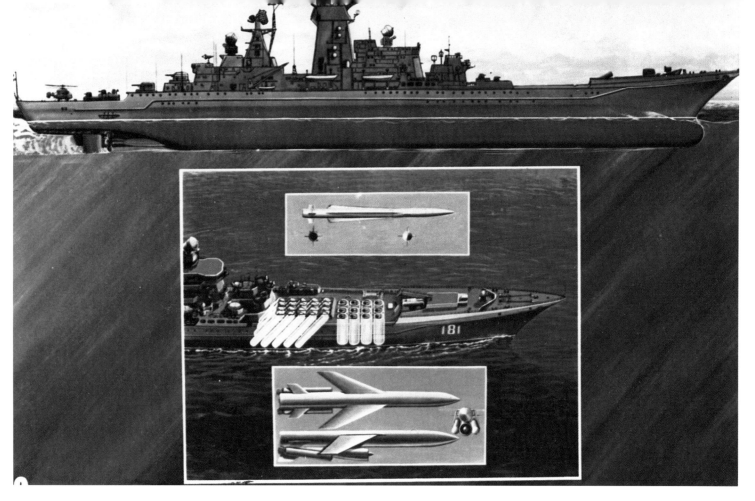

Cut-away showing the firing tube layout of a 'Kirov' class nuclear-powered cruiser. There are 20 launch tubes for 20 SS-N-19 surface-to-surface missiles and 12 launch tubes for up to 96 SA-N-6 surface-to-air missiles.

The McDonnell Douglas RGM-84A Harpoon is a medium-range anti-ship cruise missile. It is one of the West's most important naval missiles, with a top speed of 615 mph (984 km/h) at sea level and a range of 70 miles (112 km).

striking the water, as the torpedo commences its homing run.
Warhead: Mk 44 or 46 lightweight acoustic homing torpedo; length: 11 ft (3.4 m); speed: subsonic.

Sea Cat (Great Britain)

Carried by destroyers and frigates, Sea Cat is a close-range anti-aircraft missile (surface-to-air), guided manually by the aimer using a joy stick but Mks 21 and 22 have radar systems that supply an auto-follow. It can also be a surface-to-surface weapon.
Warhead: high explosive; length: 4 ft 10 in (1.47 m); range: nearly 3 miles (5 km); weight: 140 lb (64 kg).

Sea Dart (Great Britain)

Carried on ASW (Anti-submarine and warfare aircraft carriers) and destroyers, this ramjet-propelled, ship-based surface-to-air and surface missile is a medium-range weapon capable of intercepting aircraft and air-to-surface missiles. Radar-controlled, it uses a computer for target selection and data handling.
Warhead: high explosive; length: 14 ft 3½ in (4.36 m); range: 20 miles (32 km) or more; weight: 1,210 lb (550 kg).

Sea Skua (Great Britain)

Launched from a Lynx helicopter, the Sea Skua is a 'sea-skimming' anti-ship missile, which, although it can cause serious damage to larger vessels, is mainly seen as a weapon against fast patrol boats.
Warhead: 44 lb (20 kg) high explosives; length: 9 ft 3½ in (2.83 m); weight: 325 lb (148 kg); range: about 9 miles (14 km).

Sea Wolf (Great Britain)

This cruise missile, carried by Type 22 frigates, is either a surface-to-air, or surface-to-surface missile capable of destroying hostile aircraft and taking out missiles, using its radar control and guidance.
Warhead: high explosive; length: 6 ft 7 in (1.98 m); weight: 176 lb (80 kg); speed: supersonic.

Martel (Great Britain/France)

Two versions of this air-to-surface missile are in service: one an anti-radar version, the other a television-guided version. The anti-radar, all-weather missile is capable of attacking a wide range of targets, but its main task is destroying enemy radars, on which it automatically homes. The television version provides the operator with a continuous picture.
Warhead: 330 lb (150 kg) high explosive; length: 13 ft 6½ in (4.13 m); weight: 1,168 lb (531 kg); range: around 20 miles (32 km); speed: subsonic.

143

A General Dynamics Tomahawk cruise missile is fired from USS Merrill, a 'Spruance' class guided-missile destroyer. This class is fitted with two quadruple container launchers.

How a Cruise Missile Operates

The battle between cruise missile and warship missile defence goes on. Modern warships, with radars, sensing devices and surface-to-air missiles, are constantly seeking new ways to protect themselves from missile attack. And the designers of missiles are continuously seeking ways of outwitting these defence systems. To counter early-warning countermeasures and decoys, cruise missiles have to be launched outside the range of a ship's radar, and descend until they skim the surface of the sea, below the warship's radar horizon amid the sea radar clutter. Even so, missiles may be detected during the pre-launch period, or by stray radiation from the missile system, so sensitive are ships' defensive devices.

The missile, once launched from an aircraft or ship, is guided by information

fed into its onboard computer prior to its release. Then, once within radar range of the target, the radar seeker automatically switches itself on and locks on to the target. It then becomes a battle of wits between the ship's electronic defences and the missile's ability to 'burn through' the jamming techniques, a radar battle which is vital for a successful attack. A missile may be launched from a high altitude or at sea level, depending on the situation.

Many missiles are propelled by turbojet engines that produce a high subsonic speed in all weathers. They are usually constructed in a number of sections, with the active radar seeker located in the nose of the missile, along with a gyro system and the fuse. The electronic section, containing the missile control systems, altimeter and power supplies, is situated directly in front of the warhead. Lastly, there are the fuel and turbojet propulsion units.

Polaris Missiles

Once a practical nuclear-powered submarine had been built which was able to stay submerged for months on end on the sea bed, the next requirement was to devise a weapon that could be fired from it as it lay underwater. The development of such a weapon owes much to the German rocket industry of the Second World War which produced the VII ballistic missile. Because its motors were powered by liquid fuel, the VII was found unsuitable for use at sea, but the vast strides made in solid-fuel development soon solved that problem. This led to the Polaris medium-range ballistic missile, which was first launched in 1960. Its range of 1,200 nautical miles was, however, considered unsatisfactory and the United States Navy pressed for a range of 2,500 nautical miles. This was achieved by the A3s in 1963. The earlier versions, A1 and A2, were single-warhead missiles, but the A3 carries three thermo-nuclear warheads having a total 600-kiloton yield. With a speed of 6,600 mph (10,560 km/h), this 32-ft (10-m) long, 35,000-lb (1,590-kg) missile has a range of 2,875 miles (4,600 km), and as the furthest point on land from sea is only 1,700 miles (2,720 km), every city and industrial complex in the world is at risk. The missile is launched from its silo on the submarine by steam, the rocket motors igniting as it breaks the surface of the sea. The pressure from the rocket's downblast compresses the water which acts as a launching pad. Nuclear submarines can carry 16 of these weapons in their silos.

A further version of the Polaris was the Poseidon missile. This 65,000-lb (29,550-kg) weapon, each one carrying between 10 and 14 50-kiloton warheads, can engage several targets using a single missile. This was followed by the equally large Trident, also armed with multiple nuclear warheads, but with a range of 4,600 miles (7,360 km). Naturally the Soviet Union has not remained inactive in this field, and although little is known about Soviet missiles, their underwater missiles are at least equal to the most advanced American ones.

These are the weapons, too fearful to contemplate. At present there is no method of detecting a submarine laying motionless on the sea bed; thus there is no defensive counter to it. Each submarine can deliver the equivalent of over 10,000,000 tons (10,160,000 tonnes) of high explosive.

The ultimate naval missile
must be the Trident
submarine-launched strategic
ballistic missile. It has seven
Mk4 MIRVs (Multiple
Independently-Targeted Re-
entry Vehicles) each with a
W76 100 kiloton warhead
and a reported range of
4,350 miles (6,960 km).

ATTACK FROM BELOW

Down the centuries naval commanders have been aware that the most vulnerable part of a ship lay below the waterline, open to silent, unseen attack by a vessel capable of operating from under the surface. When such a weapon did present itself, most of them were horrified at its possibilities and shunned it use. In revolutionary France, French admirals saw in Robert Fulton's submarine, a weapon so terrible that their consciences would not allow them to agree to its use. Napoleon and William Pitt both saw its devastating potential as a weapon, but the former lost interest and the latter was overruled by his admirals who narrowly defined naval warfare in terms of heavily gunned 'ships-of-the-line'. Gradually fleet commanders came to accept the submarine and by the beginning of the First World War it was looked upon by some as the answer to the battleship.

Like the battleship, the submarine is not a weapon in itself, but a platform for a weapon. The big gun became the main armament of the former and the 'loco-motive torpedo' was adapted to arm the submarine. Until nuclear-powered craft appeared, the submarine was never a truly underwater vessel. Whereas nuclear submarines can cruise at high speeds, submerged for months on end, conventional submarines are really surface craft able to submerge and cruise for a limited period at low speeds. The need to surface to renew the air in the boat, to recharge the electric motor batteries and to transmit and receive radio information makes them vulnerable targets during this surfacing period. It was this fundamental disability which brought about the eventual failure of the U-Boat in the Second World War. With no such problem, the Polaris submarine, armed with intercontinental ballistic missiles, has become the ultimate weapon at sea. It is

astonishing that such a fearfully efficient and technically brilliant weapon could have been developed in less than a hundred years.

Early Submersibles

Since ancient times attempts have been made to construct an underwater craft, and one improbable idea followed another, the majority never leaving the drawing board. Although a number of more or less practical submersibles were built, the designers never really got to grips with the main problems facing underwater vessels:
1. An adequate supply of air to enable the boat to operate for a militarily practical time submerged.
2. An efficient engine to drive the vessel on the surface.
3. A separate engine to drive the boat underwater.
4. A means of conning from below the surface.
5. Good depth-keeping qualities.
6. A powerful weapon to be used while submerged.
7. To ensure a steady flow of volunteers to a submarine service, a means of escape had to be found should the boat be sunk.

The spar torpedo, used on hand-propelled Confederate 'Davids' during the American Civil War, was as dangerous to the crew of the submarine as it was to the enemy ship, and it was not until Robert Whitehead designed his 'locomotive torpedo' that the submarine became a serious menace. By the First World War Whitehead torpedoes were usually 18 in (46 cm) or 21 in (53 cm) in diameter, 17.5 or 22 ft (5.3 or 6.7 m) respectively in length, with a range of 3,750 yd (3,430 m) at 44 knots and 10,000 yd (9,144 m) at 28 knots.

Another American nuclear submarine is launched to join the steadily growing fleet.

Submarines themselves by 1915 were driven by a surface engine (diesels had become standard) to reach 15.5 to 17.5 knots; separate twin electric battery motors gave speeds of from 5 to 9 knots submerged, and they were able to be trimmed easily to compensate for the loss of weight as torpedoes were fired. Their range was approximately 8,500 miles (13,600 km) on the surface and around 72 miles (115 km) submerged for 16 hours, when they had to surface to renew their air and recharge their batteries. These 750 tonners (830 tons submerged) were armed with two to four 20-in (50-cm) bow torpedo tubes and one or two stern tubes.

The First World War

At the outbreak of the First World War, the German Navy saw the U-Boat mainly as a reconnaissance weapon, but they soon realized its potential as a lethal attack weapon. Although the Germans enjoyed early successes against heavy British units [*Kapitän Leutnant* Otto Weddingen sank the 12,000-ton (12,200-tonne) heavy cruisers, *Aboukir, Crecy* and *Hogue* in quick succession off the Dutch coast in 1914] they appreciated that the submarine's real threat lay in a *guerre de course* against British shipping. At first the U-Boat could be destroyed only by ramming or gunfire on the surface, and astute submarine commanders rarely surfaced during the daytime. Below the water they were invisible except for the tell-tale periscope wake when conning a target. One by one, new detection methods, anti-submarine weapons and convoy techniques limited the activities of the U-Boats, but not before they had sunk 12,850,814 tons (13,056,427 tonnes) of Allied shipping, representing 5,531 ships. But new methods of detection and attack

had taken their toll; by the end of the war the German U-Boat arm had lost 178 boats, 50 per cent of its complement, and 40 per cent of its crews, 5,364 officers and men. This pattern repeated itself in the Second World War: at one stage the tonnage of Allied merchantmen sunk rose to 650,000 tons (660,400 tonnes) a *month* – rapidly approaching the 800,000 tons (812,800 tonnes) a month calculated by Admiral Dönitz, Commander-in-Chief of the U-Boat arm, as the figure necessary to bring Great Britain to her knees. By 1943 more efficient U-Boat hunting techniques had swung the pendulum in the other direction; 200 U-Boats were lost during that year for a dramatic fall in the tonnage of shipping sunk. This cat-and-mouse situation has persisted down to the present time: new ideas in submarine warfare countered by new hunting tactics and methods of detection and attack.

ANTI-SUBMARINE ACTION – FIRST WORLD WAR

Once the Germans fully realized the 'hitting' power of a U-Boat, they developed it into an unseen menace capable of sending even the proud battleship to the bottom. Little thought had been given to the tactical use of the submarine, and none at all to means of detecting and combating it. The only hope for the Allies in the early stages of the First World War was to ram U-Boats or destroy them with superior gunfire. This presupposed catching them on the surface, and U-Boat commanders soon learned the values of a constant look-out and the crash dive. Two other methods of coping with the underwater menace were quickly introduced: minefields and nets (later these were strung with small contact mines). Although passive they accounted for 25 per cent of U-Boats sunk during the war. The first attacking weapon to be used against submarines with any marked effect was the depth-charge.

War is a great spur to invention, particularly when mounting merchant-shipping losses spell economic collapse, and by late 1915 the first of a number of different hydrophones came into being. These were, quite simply, underwater listening devices which were made directional to pick the sound of a U-Boat's propeller noise. UC.7 became the first victim of a combined attack of the new sensor coupled with depth-charges. The detonation of 300 lb (136 kg) of high explosive (the force of an explosion is more than doubled in water) could be disastrous to a U-Boat especially if the charge exploded directly below it.

Among the many strange ideas that the Admiralty received on combating the submarine menace, the most bizarre was the plan to train seagulls to locate a travelling periscope. A dummy periscope was to be trailed through the water with a container which scattered fish around it. The theory was that once the birds associated a periscope with food, they would naturally flock to the real ones. The inventor made no mention of how sufficient numbers of 'trained' seagulls would be obtained to cover the wastes of the Atlantic and the North Sea.

On a more serious note, explosive sweeps were towed behind fast destroyers armed with an electric indicator which showed any underwater obstruction; the charge could then be detonated from the ship. When U-Boats took to attacking the trawler fishing fleet in the North Sea, one trawler in the fleet often towed an old 'C'-class submarine connected by telephone. As soon as the German surfaced, his bearing was given to the 'C' boat, who slipped free and manoeuvred into position to fire a torpedo. Despite minor successes, these ideas did little to stem the tide of mounting shipping losses and other means of countering U-Boat warfare were desperately sought.

To fight against the U-Boat threat, a number of merchantmen were converted into 'Q' ships. Pictured here with her guns concealed is the famous HMS Hyderabad.

A further method, and one that proved quite successful in the beginning, was the legendary 'Q' ship tactic. As the cost of torpedoes increased, U-Boat commanders chose to surface to sink single unarmed merchant ships by gunfire from their 4-in deck gun. The Allies argued that if a small merchantman, hardly large enough to justify a torpedo, were armed with a concealed gun, she could catch a U-Boat unawares as she surfaced, and sink her before her gun's crew could go into action. The armament was concealed behind shutters which fell away to reveal a 4-in gun. Sailing under the Red or Blue Ensign, her crew dressed in 'civvies', she would run up the White Ensign just before opening up. At the first sign of a U-Boat, 'panic parties' would take the ship's boats leaving the concealed gun crew closed up for action. As the unsuspecting U-Boat manoeuvred into position, the shutters would fall away and the quick-firing 4-in gun would go into action. Unfortunately, although the first few victims were easily trapped, one U-Boat escaped to pass the information on to her base, and from then onwards the 'Q' ship was not a success. In 1917, with the U-Boat campaign at its height, they were withdrawn. Often the holds of 'Q' ships were loaded with timber to give added buoyancy should the submarine commander decide to risk a torpedo. A mark of the risk involved is reflected in the fact that the most successful 'Q' ship commander, Captain Gordon

Campbell, was awarded the Victoria Cross in 1916 for his success. In spite of their limited successes in the First World War, 'Q' ships, for security reasons designated 'freighters', were tried in the Second World War, with even less success; not one of the six commissioned even saw a U-Boat, and when two were sunk by torpedoes, they were withdrawn in 1941.

With a long history of success dating back to the twelfth century, it is surprising that convoy tactics were not employed before 1917, a failure in established naval tactics that all but lost the war for the Allies. Concentrating merchantmen in a convoy forced the U-Boats to attack at one point: no longer could they lie in wait across a known shipping lane for a victim. This allowed part of the convoy escort, destroyers, sloops, and other patrol craft to hunt out and attack, which they did with ever-growing success. Once an adequate escort system evolved, merchant shipping sinkings fell away dramatically. Of the 84,000 ships that sailed under convoy, only 257, or less than 0.4 per cent were lost to submarine attack, while U-Boat losses rose alarmingly. By adopting a pre-arranged zig-zag course, not easy in rough seas and murky weather, convoys made it even more difficult for U-Boat commanders to score a hit without taking greater risks, and with their underwater speed a maximum 9 knots, gave them only split seconds to calculate the run of the 'fish'.

The 'Q' ships were manned by Royal Navy crews. The officers and men are pictured here wearing their uniforms, although on patrol they wore civilian rig.

Between the Wars

The submarine had made the First World War ruinously expensive for the Allies, apart from virtually bringing them to their knees. The Treaty of Versailles, they believed, ensured that Germany would never have another U-Boat fleet, while they themselves strengthened their submarine services. Strangely enough, although the large cruiser submarine had proved of little value in the First World War, the navies of the world plumped for bigger and bigger boats with heavier armament and provision for scouting aircraft. Great Britain commissioned the 2,425-ton (2,464-tonne) XI, with a range of 12,400 miles (19,840 km) on the surface: the U.S.A. came out with the 2,730-ton (2,774-tonne) *Narwhal*, and the Japanese with the 2,135-ton (2,169-tonne) *I1*; but the French went one better with the *Surcouf*. Displacing 2,888 tons (2,934 tonnes), (4,304 tons/4,373 tonnes submerged), she was the largest submarine in the world, armed with twin 8-in guns as well as her 18 21.7-in (55-cm) torpedoes (with ten reloads) and four 15.7-in (40-cm). She also carried a scouting plane housed in a cylindrical hanger abaft the conning tower. Once again, however, the most successful submarines during the Second World War were the 750 to 1,000 tonners (760 to 1,020 metric tonners); the German Type VII U-Boat hardly differed from her First World War counterparts. Armed with five 21-in (53-cm) tubes and a 4-in deck gun, she had a range of 6,500 surface miles (10,400 km) at 12 knots; submerged, 72 miles (115 km) at 4 knots. Her top speeds were still only 17.2 knots on the surface and 8 knots submerged. Yet once again she nearly starved out Great Britain.

Life aboard a U-Boat was hard; designed

The famous French submarine Surcouf *was the largest submarine built between the wars. She was armed with two 8-in guns, torpedo tubes and also had an aircraft hangar, abaft the conning tower for a spotter floatplane.*

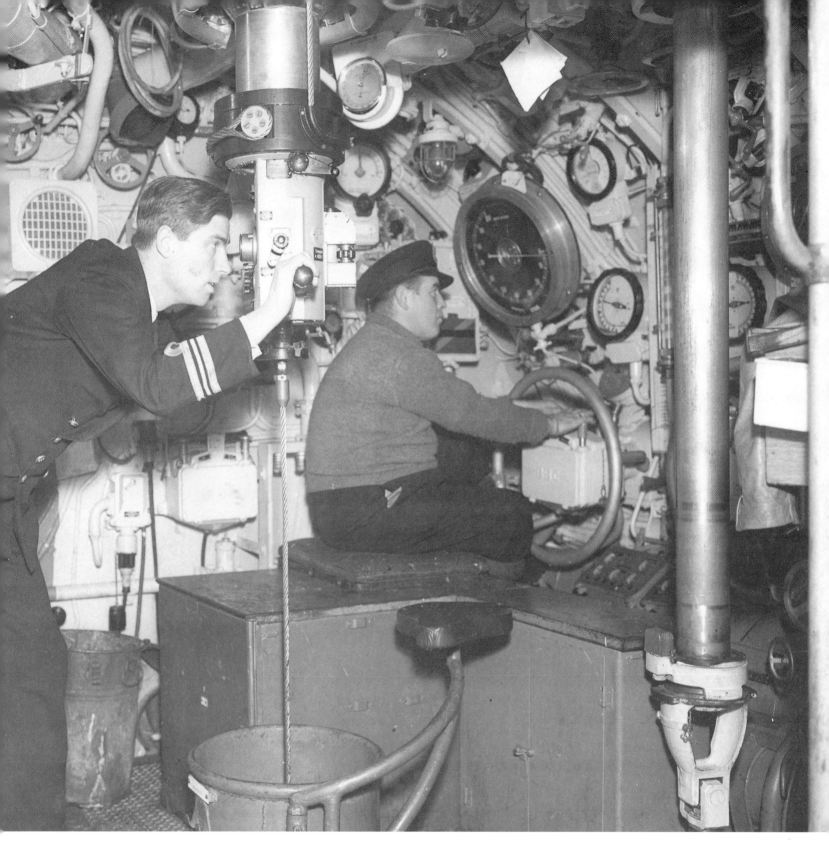

for action not for comfort, everything was subordinated to her fighting ability. She was a platform for delivering her deadly 'fish', nothing more. Unlike the British and American who built their submarines to last, the *Kriegsmarine* were happy for them to last through a war, so the crews were hardly pampered, although the food was the best that could be provided. Conditions were appalling; clothes and personal possessions were stowed in every odd space – behind pipes, under bunks (which never grew cold, the off-watch crew tum-

bled in as the new watch scrambled out). At the beginning of each voyage a false deck made up of boxes of tinned stores was created down the cramped passage-ways. After several hours submerged, the air became foul with the stench of fuel oil, cooking, sweat and, in rough weather, vomit. A good commander would see to it that all crew members were allowed a few gulps of fresh air on the conning tower when the boat surfaced to recharge her batteries and clear the atmosphere. Gramophone records were played most

A British officer scans through the periscope of HMS Graph. The submarine had originally been the German submarine U.570, until her capture.

mealtimes, but British music and American jazz was officially banned, although this depended very much on the individual commander and whether the boat was carrying a Nazi Party political officer.

The Second World War

The U-Boat arm had dramatic success at the beginning of the Second World War; by 1942 the Allies were losing over 100 ships a month. But from then onwards, there was an equally dramatic fall in the number of ships sunk, and a corresponding rise in the number of U-Boats destroyed.

The Royal Navy had not made the same mistake twice – this time the navy had employed a convoy system from the outset. However naval officials were overconfident about the ability of Asdic and depth-charges to deal with any U-Boat attacks. They also had not considered Admiral Dönitz, the Commander-in-Chief of the U-Boat arm, a dedicated submariner and a brilliant tactician. He had pinpointed the weakness of the First World War campaign and had rectified it. U-Boats had spent too much time searching out convoys and

The 'messing' aboard the confined quarters of HMS Graph before the end of the Second World War.

individual ships and attacking singly. He reasoned that if they attacked as a group, with an element of surprise, they could wreak havoc among the merchantmen of even the most strongly escorted convoy – the 'wolf-pack' came into being. U-Boats took up an extended line of search, sailing slowly towards the most likely courses taken by east-bound Atlantic convoys. Once a convoy had been located, the U-Boat made a sighting report and, diving deep, took up station behind the convoy to shadow. The attack began when the wolf-pack was concentrated in force at an agreed position. New tactics, devised by emerging submarine aces such as Otto Kretschmer of *U.99*, Joachim Schepke, of *U.100* and Gunther Prien of *U.47* (who sank the *Royal Oak* as she lay at anchor in the naval base at Scapa Flow in October 1939), made the Asdic of the British escorts virtually useless. The very strength of Asdic was its failing. An Anglo-French echo-sounding device, developed after the First World War, that bounced sound waves off a submerged object, it was useless on the surface, and furthermore, it could only operate below a certain depth. By

Overleaf: A U-Boat on the surface in a rough Atlantic sea. As the war progressed the U-Boats had to spend more daylight hours below the waves to escape detection by long-range Allied aircraft.

A painting of the presentation of the Knight's Cross to a successful U-Boat ace.

attacking at night on the surface, the U-Boats, with their low profiles, were all but invisible and left the convoy escorts helpless to protect their flock. Kretschmer, who claimed the biggest total of all, more than 500,000 tons (508,000 tonnes) of Allied shipping, actually took his boat into the convoy itself, sailing down the lines of ships, picking off victims. By 1942 the Allies had lost over 16,090,697 tons

(16,348,148 tonnes) of shipping. Things were looking serious as Dönitz's target of 800,000 tons (812,800 tonnes) a month was approached. But here, as in the First World War, the *Kriegsmarine* was guilty of a gross strategical error – it had not allowed for new Allied tactics, new counter-measures.

Horrified at their mounting shipping losses, the British tried every means to escape depth-charge attack. It was also during 1941 that *U.110* was taken on the surface, and a boarding party was able to recover her code books before she was scuttled. Although kept a close secret until well after the war, there is reason to believe that a knowledge of *Kriegsmarine* cyphers played a part in the destruction of many U-Boats.

As an interim answer to the giant Focke Wolf Kondor, Sea Hurricanes were catapulted off the forecastles of merchantmen; later the escort carrier was introduced. Once the U.S.A. entered the war with its enormous shipbuilding facilities, escort carriers began to roll off the slipways and from that time onwards the German U-Boat campaign was doomed. The United States itself, however, was not equipped for anti-submarine warfare, in spite of the experience gained in the First World War, and until the U.S. moved into top gear, U-Boat commanders enjoyed enormous success. Moving to the Caribbean and the eastern seaboard of the United States, the German U-Boats found easy pickings until the U.S. Navy eventually introduced a convoy system – in six months 21 U-Boats had destroyed 500 merchant ships.

On paper Dönitz's U-Boats were poised for victory, but even with commitments in the Pacific, the United States's shipbuilding potential spelt long-term disaster for the *Kriegsmarine*. This, coupled with increased intervention from aircraft fitted with a short wave radar set (ASV – Air to Surface Vessel), tipped the scales and U-Boat losses grew at an alarming rate. Anti-aircraft weapons were crammed onto the U-Boats in an effort to fight back at the Sunderlands and Liberators, but experienced pilots soon found ways to avoid the galling AA fire. Circling the U-Boat, beyond range of her AA guns, the aircraft simply called up the nearest surface warship to take over the attack. Should the submarine attempt to dive, the aircraft swept down to blow her out of the water with bombs and depth-charges. The 'Battle of Seconds' began, as the German gunners scrambled to get below in 30 or 40 seconds before the conning tower hatch slammed shut and the boat began her dramatic crash dive.

U-Boat losses rocketed. In early 1943, as shipping losses decreased, the U-Boat campaign was doomed to failure, despite

counter them. In 1984 the first Type 271 surface radar was introduced; it was able to pick up a U-Boat's conning tower at over 2.6 miles (4.0 km). This was followed by the 'Huff-Duff', High Frequency Direction Finding (H/F-D/F). A small sensitive set installed aboard an escort ship, 'Huff Duff' allowed her to pinpoint signals from a shadowing U-Boat to within a quarter of a mile, forcing the submarine to dive deep to

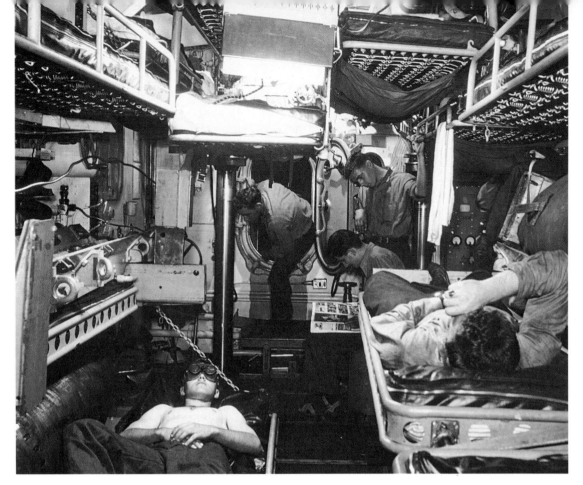

The cramped interior of this American Second World War submarine was still spacious compared with the German boats. (Note the man under a sun lamp.)

An Italian submarine surrenders to the Allies at Salerno at the end of the Italian phase of the war.

SHIPPING AND U-BOAT LOSSES IN EARLY 1943			
Month	Shipping sunk		U-Boats destroyed
	tons	tonnes	
April	245,000	249,000	15
May	165,000	168,000	40
June	118,000	120,000	17
July	123,000	125,000	37
	651,000	662,000	109

Opposite: The submarine war was as fierce in the Pacific. Here, an American Chief Petty Officer is supervising the loading of a torpedo.

the last-ditch introduction of new homing torpedoes and revolutionary submarines.

Escort vessels (destroyers, frigates and corvettes) were fitted with extra depth-charge throwers, improved hurling, more powerful charges, and the 'Hedgehog' spigot mortar appeared. This 24-barrel mortar, mounted on the forecastle of an escort fired simultaneously 35-lb (16-kg) charges of Torpex (along with Minol, a new and more powerful explosive) over a predetermined spread. Firing ahead of the ship allowed sonar contact right up to the last minute, whereas when depth-charges were dropped from the stern, contact was lost as the ship passed over the submarine.

MIDGET SUBMARINES AND HUMAN TORPEDOES

Although midget submarines and manned torpedoes had no great influence on the war at sea, there were many notable single achievements. As early as the First World War, the Italian Navy had turned its attention to human torpedoes, 'maiali' or 'pigs'. Not a torpedo in the strict sense of the world, the *maiale* consisted of a tediously slow – it had an underwater speed of only 2 to 3 knots – electrically propelled 'chariot', crewed by a pilot and diver, which carried a 660-lb (300-kg) detachable warhead. Among the successes of the Small Weapons Unit of the Italian Navy with its SLC – *siluro a lenta corsa* (slow running torpedo) – was the sinking, in 1941, of the British battleships HMS *Vanguard* and HMS *Queen Elizabeth* as they lay in harbour at Alexandria in Egypt.

The Japanese suicide *'Kaiten'* (Heaven Shakers), introduced in the closing stages of the war in the Pacific, were in fact true torpedoes, crewed by a single man. Developed from the oxygen-driven 'Long Lance' torpedo and carrying a 3,000-lb (1,400-kg) warhead, it was capable of covering 14 miles (22 km) at 30 knots, when launched from an 'I' class submarine. Over the last 500 yd (460 m) to its target it accelerated to 40 knots. In practice very few ships were sunk, for the loss of eight 2,135-ton (2,170-tonne) 'I' class cruiser submarines and most of the 'Kaiten' put into operation.

Great Britain and Germany, in the main, concentrated on producing midget submarines, manned by one, two or four crewmembers and launched close to their targets by parent submarines. German midgets ('K' craft) were chiefly seen as means of holding up surface vessels in the expected Invasion of Europe, but they met with little success. On the other hand, the British 'X' craft, armed with two 1,000-lb (455-kg) detachable side-chargers, were very much an attack weapon. Their most notable feat was to put the battleship *Tirpitz* out of action in a Norwegian fjord, causing her to be taken south for repairs where she came within range of R.A.F. bombers which sank her.

The British 'X' craft 25 underway. It was this type of submarine that attacked the Tirpitz.

Allied naval personnel examine a German midget submarine at the end of the war.

The Postwar Scramble

As soon as the war was over, the Allies became involved in an undignified scramble to lay their hands on existing equipment, experimental ideas and key personnel – especially rocket engineers. Among the German shipyards and naval bases, Allied intelligence officers discovered some Type XXI and Walther boats that had neither been destroyed by bombing nor deliberately sabotaged. Dönitz had promised Hitler great things from these boats and Great Britain, the United States and the Soviet Union were anxious to study them in the light of their own projected submarine fleets.

Although the schnorkel, a Dutch invention for running diesels at periscope depth, had been introduced, German designers were hard at work on an engine that could achieve high speeds while submerged with-

out using oxygen – the result was the Walther engine, invented by Dr. Helmut Walther. This propulsion system was basically a method of driving a close-circuit gas turbine by burning an oxidant with fuel oil, thus eliminating the need for a supply of atmospheric oxygen. Using a concentrated form of hydrogen peroxide, Perhydrol, it generated far more power than conventional electrically driven motors, promising speeds in excess of 25 knots. It had been greeted at the time as the 'true' submarine, able to operate underwater without having to come periodically to the surface for air, and considerable pressure was exercised by the U-Boat command to put it into commission as quickly as possible. It did, however, have serious faults, faults, moreover, that were never overcome during the extensive experiments carried out after the war. As well as being eight times the cost of conventional oil and able to give only an

underwater range of 80 miles (128 km) at full speed, the fuel for this motor was also highly volatile and liable to explode if any impurities found their way into the storage tanks.

The British, rechristening *U.1407* HMS *Meteorite*, tested her for four years, and then built two improved versions, *Explorer* and *Excalibur*. These peroxide boats, naturally nicknamed 'blondes', were finally abandoned as being only 75 per cent safe, much to the relief of their crews – explosions had been reported aboard, and a leak of noxious fumes had also been rumoured. The Soviets, too, had acquired a Walther boat and although it is known that they ran tests on her and even possibly built prototypes, no results of their experiments have ever been disclosed. The Americans, however, showed no interest. Their research carried out during the production of the atom bomb had convinced them that nuclear fission could be harnessed and used to produce mechanical energy.

The Type XXI had a greater bearing on the development of postwar submarines than the temperamental Walther boats. In reality this was a brilliant redesign of a standard submarine making the most of all its good points and eliminating the bad ones. Battery capacity was trebled to raise the submerged speed to 15.5 knots, with auxiliary motors for 'silent running' at 5 knots. The deck gun was dispensed with and the usual conning tower, cluttered with platforms and standards, was streamlined into a 'fin'; indeed, the whole boat was streamlined to cut down underwater drag. Hitting capacity was speeded up by better torpedo capacity and mechanical loading techniques. This boat, looked upon by Dönitz as only an interim stop-gap until the Walther boat came into production, became the blueprint for conventional submarine design among the world's navies, including the Soviet Union, which was beginning to take naval power seriously.

The Second World War had seen not only the demise of big-gun surface craft but the end of British naval supremacy; the American super-carrier was now the most powerful weapon afloat, and the U.S. Navy by far the most powerful influence at sea. The Soviet Navy, finding itself in no position to compete with the United States in the production of surface ships – the U.S.S.R. had neither the expertise nor shipbuilding facilities – turned to building a projected 1,200-strong submarine fleet as a top priority, based mainly on the German Type XXI boat. Torn between its wartime contention that sea power played only a marginal part in the defeat of the Axis and Stalin's support for a deep-sea fleet for political reasons, the Soviet Navy in 1945 put forward a 20-year construction programme of cruisers, destroyers and submarines, which really did not get off the ground until 1949/50.

After 1950 submarine construction in the Soviet Union rose alarmingly. Prior to then it had been a trickle, 12 boats a year. This was stepped up to between 60 and 80 boats, and by 1958 it was estimated that the Soviet submarine fleet had 475 submarines of all types in service – a total greater than the U-Boat arm ever had – though this number was inflated by a number of boats left over from the Second World War.

A German Type XXI submarine under construction at the Deschimag submarine factory, Bremen, at the end of the war. This design was to have a major impact on postwar submarine building.

THE NUCLEAR SUBMARINE

During the early 1930s, designers and shipbuilders were searching for the means of turning the submarine, a surface ship which could travel underwater for a short time, into a 'true' underwater craft, one whose *natural* home was below the waves. The problem, although simply defined, was anything but simple to solve. To obtain relatively fast speeds underwater called for an engine more powerful than the current electric ones. Existing conventional engines that could reach the required speeds, diesels and so on, all needed precious oxygen to operate, which would cut down a submarine's underwater life to practically nil.

At the United States Naval Research Laboratory, Dr. Ross Gunn led a team to research not only fuels that contained their own oxygen but the engines to burn them to generate power. Among the welter of ideas, the group investigated the use of alcohol as a fuel, hydrogen peroxide motors and steam turbines, but all were rejected, although the steam turbine was a distinct possibility if a means could be found to turn water into steam. Meanwhile, in Germany, Dr. Helmut Walther was working along the same lines, but concentrating on the use of hydrogen peroxide with fuel oil. Gunn dismissed this idea, but the German persisted and by the end of the Second World War his idea for peroxide-driven U-Boats was put into production.

The American team, however, was more interested in the discovery by scientists in the mid-1930s that energy radiating from the sun and stars was caused by the release of nuclear energy. Limitless energy was at hand, if only a means could be found to release and harness it. Then, in 1938, German researchers discovered nuclear fission. When uranium atoms are bombarded with neutrons, a few atoms split into two parts releasing tremendous amounts of energy.

Gunn was quick to realize that this might be the answer to a submarine's propulsion problem, and persuaded the United States government to make him a grant. The beggarly $1,500 it came up with, nevertheless, was the first money devoted to research into nuclear fission and allowed Gunn to continue his investigations.

Throughout the war, work went on, in conjunction with other researchers and institutions, in a search for a method of isolating the elusive isotope. (Later, the research was taken over by the Manhattan Engineering District, much to the chagrin of Dr. Gunn, but he was given a Civilian Service award at the end of the war for his part in the development of the atom bomb.)

For some time attempts had been made to build a nuclear reactor to fit into the hull of an existing submarine. Events were not moving fast enough for Gunn and in 1947 he resigned, disgusted at the way the United States Navy was dragging its feet. Later that year the Navy sent a contingent under Hyman C. Rickover, a naval officer, to the Nuclear Research Center at Oakville, Tennessee. Rickover, a dynamic personality, bullied the newly formed Atomic Energy Commission into accelerating the nuclear submarine effort, and in August 1951 they awarded a contract to the Electric Boat Company to construct the first nuclear submarine.

A nuclear reactor produces heat energy through the fission of uranium atoms. As this consumes only a very small amount of uranium and requires little or no oxygen, this is the perfect propulsion system for a submarine. As President Harry S. Truman said at the laying of the keel of the first nuclear submarine, 'A few ounces of uranium will give her ample fuel to travel thousands of miles at top speed.' He went on to say, 'She will be able to stay underwater indefinitely. Her atomic engine will permit her to be completely free of the earth's atmosphere.

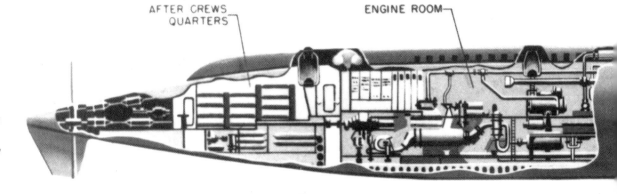

AFTER CREWS QUARTERS

ENGINE ROOM

Cut-away of the world's first nuclear sea-going vessel, the USS Nautilus, *showing how spacious she was in comparison to First and Second World War submarines.*

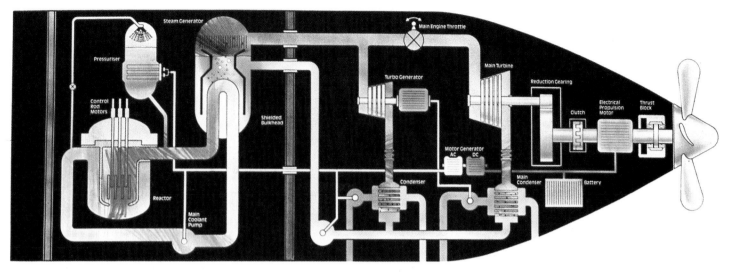

She will not even require a breathing tube [schnorkel] to the surface.' Heat is transferred to a steam generator by a primary coolant, usually pressurized water in most submarines. This becomes radioactive as it loops through the reactor. Within the steam generator the heat is transmitted to a secondary system, creating steam, which is then used to drive the turbines, spinning the submarine's propeller shaft. In transferring the heat from the reactor to the steam generator, the pressurized water is cooled and, in its turn, cools down the core of the reactor, while picking up heat for the next cycle.

The keel of the world's first nuclear submarine, USS *Nautilus*, was laid down at Groton, Connecticut, on 14 June 1952. At the time it was estimated that she would move underwater at a speed of 20 knots. A month later a contract was given to the Electric Boat Company to construct a second NUC, USS *Seawolf* (SSN-575), that would use sodium to transfer heat from the reactor to the steam generator. Nearly two years later, *Nautilus* slid down the slipway,

launched by the wife of President Eisenhower. The submarine, 320 ft (98 m) in length with a surface displacement of 3,530 tons (3,590 tonnes), got underway for the first time on 17 January 1954, making the historic signal, 'Underway on nuclear power'. A total revolution in naval sea power had occurred.

In May 1954 *Nautilus* made her maiden voyage to San Juan, Puerto Rico – submerged – a distance of 1,381 miles (2,210 km) at an average speed of 16 knots, well below her officially announced top speed of 23 knots; her successors were able to achieve much higher speeds. Her reactor core was replaced after she had travelled 62,562 miles (100,099 km). [An equivalent distance travelled by a conventional submarine would have burned over two million gallons (nine million litres) of diesel oil.] Her second core took her further; her third, 150,000 miles (240,000 km). Subsequent NUCs were able to travel 400,000 miles (640,000 km) on a single core, the equivalent of ten years operational service. Her successor, USS *Seawolf*, failed to

A diagram of the typical layout of a submarine reactor and turbine. The advantage of nuclear power is that it allows a submarine to travel vast distances without having to surface.

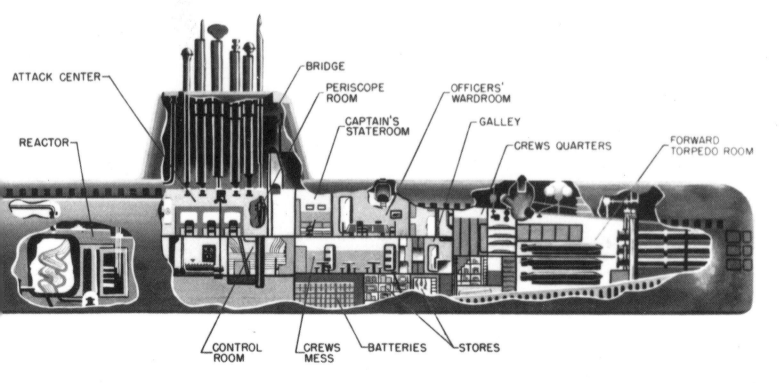

live up to expectations, the corrosive properties of her sodium coolant caused problems which never allowed her to achieve her full potential speed, but she did stay submerged for a record 60 days in 1958.

Interested in the military possibilities of operating under ice, the United States Navy began a series of probes with *Nautilus* under the Arctic pack ice. This was assisted by the introduction of a fathometer, a delicate meter for establishing the exact depth in fathoms to the sea bed and any underwater obstructions. This is one of the 'eyes' of a boat. Working on a principle similar to sonar, it bounces signals off the sea bed which are recorded as distances and transferred to a visual display unit. Sonar was used by *Nautilus* to pinpoint objects ahead and astern, but particularly upwards, to determine the clearance to the ice pack. The first of these frighteningly claustrophobic probes proving

highly successful, an attempt was made to steam under the ice cap from Alaska to emerge in the North Atlantic, a highly desirable and strategic military exercise.

Unfortunately, ice conditions frustrated the early attempts, but finally on 23 July 1958 the *Nautilus* began her historic journey under the North Pole. Steaming north from Pearl Harbor with a crew of 112 and four civilians, she slipped under the Arctic ice pack, beginning her trip into the unknown. No one knew for certain the depths and underwater formation of the inverted ice mountains that probed into the Arctic waters. The submarine would be totally at the mercy of the efficiency of her sonar equipment. It was calculated that the North Pole was above them at 1115 hours on 3 August. Steaming south the *Nautilus* made the open ocean between Greenland and Iceland after several nerve-wracking days under the ice. The military possibilities were not lost on the Soviet Navy, and soon her nuclear submarines, as well as further American ones, were probing beneath the ice.

The sodium-cooled plant aboard *Seawolf* having proved a failure, Rickover, by now an admiral, exchanged it for pressurized-water plants, which became standard for all NUCs, each one becoming that bit more efficient than the previous one. Once *Nautilus* had been 'proved', four production NUCs of the 'Skate' class were commissioned. Nuclear submarines with special roles were also commissioned: the radar picket submarine *Triton*, fitted with twin reactors; the *Halibut*, carrying Regulus missiles; and the small 'Tullibee' class of submarine hunter-killers.

The high-speed 'Skipjack' class submarines that followed, in the light of rapidly improving detection techniques which the Soviet Navy was known to have, had one serious drawback – they were too noisy; they also operated at much the same depth as Second World War submarines. Slower, quieter submarines are less liable to detection, but the increasing Soviet military threat demanded faster NUCs that could operate at lower depths to take advantage of high speeds for manoeuvrability. The costs involved in constructing such a submarine were astronomical; specially designed sound-muffling equipment would have to be installed and a heavier steel hull and internal equipment would have to be developed to withstand the enormous pressures encountered at the required operational depths – 80,000 lb/sq in (5,600 kg/sq cm). This led to the ill-fated *Thresher*, whose ballast tanks failed to save her in her fatal dive. Subsequent NUCs of the 'Lafayette', 'Sturgeon' and 'Narwhal' classes all had improved air-pressure systems for blowing ballast tanks for an emergency surfacing.

Although now getting old, the 'Skipjack' class of nuclear fleet submarines are still considered frontline vessels. This is due to their very high underwater speed which is beaten only by the 'Los Angeles' class of submarine.

USS Sturgeon *travelling at speed on the surface. Between 1963 and 1971 a total of 37 vessels of the class were built. The last nine are 10 ft (3 m) longer than the rest to permit the fitting of extra electronics.*

Opposite: A test launch of a submarine-launched General Dynamics Tomahawk cruise missile.

Commissioned in April 1964, USS Daniel Boone is a 'Lafayette' class nuclear-powered ballistic-missile submarine. She is fitted with launch tubes for 16 Trident missiles. The 'Lafayette' class has a range of 400,000 miles (640,000 km) before the nuclear core has to be replaced.

By 1970 the United States Navy had 85 nuclear submarines in operation, with the Soviet Navy running about the same number. However, whereas production of NUCs was falling in the United States, it was rising quickly in the Soviet Union. (The U.S.S.R. also had 250 modern conventional submarines in service.) As the race goes on, the Americans rely more and more on quality to compensate for Soviet quantity – faster, more efficient submarines and more effective weapons.

Among the more effective weapons is the 19 ft (6-m) long, 3,450 lb (1,570-kg) Mk 48 torpedo with a conventional high explosive warhead which has replaced the older models. This has a 20-mile (32-km) range and homing mechanisms coupled with wire guidance. The Harpoon anti-ship cruise missile, which can be fired from torpedo tubes of conventional submarines, has a range of 60 miles (96 km). Fired from its tube in an encasing capsule, it races to the surface, where the missile ignites, leaving the canister, then homes onto its target in the later stages by radar. An improved version, the Tomahawk, not only has a greater range, measured in hundreds of miles, but it can be armed with 1,000 lb (455 kg) of high explosive or a small nuclear warhead. Along with the Polaris-, Poseiden- and Trident-armed NUCs, this gives the Americans fearful hitting power, but it was the Soviets who came out with the biggest nuclear submarine ever, in 1980, the 25,000-ton (25,400-tonne) submerged, 'Typhoon' class – heavier than a pocket-battleship.

The largest submarine ever built is the Soviet Typhoon ballistic missile submarine, seen here travelling on the surface. Its 20 launch tubes are forward of the conning tower to allow room for two nuclear reactors which supply steam for two sets of geared turbines driving two five-bladed propellers. With her twin hull it is thought that there could be a separation of up to 15 ft (4.6 m) between the outer and inner hulls.

A crewmember stands watch at the controls of USS Nautilus in the mid-1950s. Very careful watch has to be maintained in order to keep an accurate global position.

INERTIAL NAVIGATION

This system is really a highly sophisticated form of the old method of dead reckoning developed after the Second World War. Initially designed for nuclear submarines, it has been adapted for certain surface ships, but the high cost of the precisely engineered electronic equipment precludes it from widespread general use at the moment.

The whole concept behind the development of the nuclear submarine is that it should be able to remain submerged for long periods undetected, so a system of navigation had to be devised that eliminated the need for the submarine to surface to fix her position – surfacing to use either hyperbolic or celestial methods subjected the submarine to the possibility of being detected. This problem was overcome by accurately plotting the submarine's diving position at the start of her voyage, then carefully measuring each subsequent change in acceleration (which can be translated by computers into speeds and distances) and in direction which, when applied to the initial position, gives the submarine's final position. The incredible accuracy of SINS (Submarine Inertial Navigation System) was established by USS *Nautilus* throughout her voyage under the Polar ice-cap, and by USS *Triton's* submerged circumnavigation of the globe when her final margin of error for the whole voyage was less than 600 ft (183 m).

A New Era

While American scientists were making every effort to produce a nuclear reactor small enough to fit into a submarine, a further step was being taken in the development of the submarine as an offensive weapon – the ballistic missile. In 1948/49 American submarines began to be fitted with sea-based strike missiles. In many ways the introduction of the nuclear-powered submarine turned the clock back to the days when the British and French were flirting with steam power, for the only way to utilize the heat generated by a reactor is to convert water into steam. The launching of the USS *Nautilus* in 1954 marked a new and more deadly era in sea warfare, one that heralded the introduction of the Polaris family of ballistic missiles. By 1952, when the hull of *Nautilus* was laid down, a suitably small nuclear water-cooled reactor had been developed, producing 15,000 hp from each of two steam turbines. She also had conventional diesel and electric propulsion units.

The *Nautilus* was big, displacing 3,530 tons (3,590 tonnes), for two reasons: firstly, to house the reactor; secondly, to provide ample accommodation for her crew of 100 who might have to stay submerged for months on end. For *Nautilus* was a 'true' submarine in every sense of the word; with a nuclear reactor consuming no oxygen, her only limitation on remaining submerged was the endurance of her crew. Her original core of uranium was replaced only after steaming 62,562 miles (100,099 km). On 3 August 1958 she created history by crossing the North Pole submerged, which called for highly sophisticated navigational aids, sonar equipment and air 'scrubbers'.

Fresh air, always a bugbear in submarines, was no problem for oxygen was drawn from the water electronically and 'scrubbers' took out the carbon dioxide; the air itself was conditioned by a plant capable of doing the job for a small town on a summer's day. There was also a plant for turning sea water into fresh drinking water. The main problems were purely psychological ones – how to keep the crew happy, indeed sane, during months lying submerged on the sea bed. To an extent this was solved by providing fairly spacious accommodation, pleasant, relaxing colour schemes, the best of food – including the inevitable ice-cream-making machines – laundries and other labour-saving devices. Off-watch entertainment was considered of cardinal importance: cinema, video, record players and a well-stocked library. Travelling under the polar ice called for pinpoint navigation and accurate sonar readings – ahead, astern, above and below – and a 'fathometer' echo-sounding system that could provide computer-precise depths.

Preoccupied with the threat of Soviet missile attack, the United States introduced seaward early-warning radar 'picket lines' of surface ships and submarines. This led to the enormous radar picket submarine *Triton*; 469 ft (143 m) long, she displaced 6,000 tons (6,100 tonnes), 8,000 tons (8,130 tonnes) submerged, and was the largest submarine to date.

The Voyage of the *Triton*

At 1730 hours on 16 February 1960, *Triton*, a heavy sea breaking over her bows, prepared to dive, the hatch slammed and the big nuclear submarine began to go under. It was the beginning of her attempt on her maiden voyage to circumnavigate the globe – submerged. She was at the St. Peter and St. Paul Rocks in the North Atlantic, the point at which she would complete her voyage. From there she would round Cape Horn into the Pacific, make towards Easter Island, on to the Philippines and then she would steer for Java. Her course from there would take her across the Indian Ocean to the Cape of Good Hope, into the South Atlantic and northwards to the Rocks.

Twenty-four hours later those aboard had their first inkling of things to come, the safety valve at the inboard end of the air vent tube jammed. Had the valve at the head of the tube failed to close as it came down from drawing in fresh air, the boat would have flooded and most probably sunk. The cause was found to be a dockyard worker's flashlight crushed in the valve casing. Within minutes, the engineer officer was reporting water coming into the engine room; the port engine would have to be stopped and its nuclear reactor closed down for an estimated five hours. Fortunately the starboard engine had sufficient power for *Triton* to keep up a fast cruising speed. Captain Beach had hardly turned in, when he was jerked awake by the insistent clanging of the nuclear alarm bell. Hastily throwing on his clothes, he hurried to the engine room to find the reactor stable – a fault had been found in the alarm system itself.

The 1 March saw them beyond the Equator, well on their way to Cape Horn. It was Jim Start, Triton's doctor, who brought the first bad news of the day, 'Captain, we have a very sick man on the boat.' Behind the doctor stood the chief engineer with more bad news; it appeared that one of the reactors which had been approaching the danger mark went beyond. There was no choice; the reactor had to be immediately closed down – the consequences in not doing so were unthinkable. Two hours later a mistake was found in the calculations; it, too, had been a false alarm. The following day, Poole, the sick rating, was violently ill; there was nothing for it but to turn north to put him aboard an American warship in the area, USS Macon. At the rendezvous the Triton came up until only the top of her sail was above the surface; technically she was still submerged. Without incident, Poole was safely taken aboard the Macon. They had travelled 2,000 miles (3,200 km) off course and several days had been lost, but once more Triton steered for Cape Horn at top speed – it was sighted on 7 March.

Triton was well on the way to Easter Island when the next incident occurred. Once again sea water was pouring into the engine room; this time through the propeller shaft. By the time Captain Beach arrived, there were over 4 in (10 cm) of water lapping over the deck, and it was becoming deeper by the minute – the pumps were unable to clear it. When the engines were stopped it was discovered that a number of locking washers had not been fitted in the shipyard.

The Cape of Good Hope was reached without incident, the captain's log reading:

Easter Sunday, 17 April, 1960

1721 set course for St. Peter and St. Paul Rocks in mid-Atlantic. Will arrive there on April 25.

0754 Crossed Equator for the fourth and last time.

A few hundred miles from the end of their circumnavigation an explosion sent oil splattering all over the engine room but this was the final trouble to be suffered by Triton. The final entry in the log reads

25 April

1500 First underwater voyage around the world now complete.

The Loss of the *Thresher*

On the morning of Tuesday 9 April 1963, Thresher, the world's most advanced nuclear submarine of its day, slipped out of Portsmouth, New Hampshire. As well as her crew of 108 officers and men, there were 21 others, experts and officials, to report on a number of trials following a refit. Outside the base they ran into a heavy sea and she began to roll; steaming towards her escort ship, USS Skylark, some of the dockyard engineers aboard Thresher were violently seasick. At 0700 hours the following morning they rendezvoused with Skylark and prepared to dive – she would be linked up by radio telephone to her escort.

The order to flood ballast tanks was given by her captain, Commander Wes Harvey. Water surged in as her engines drove her under to level out at 65 ft (20 m); her test dive was to be made at 1,000 ft (305 m), deeper than she had ever been before. At 0749 came the order 'Prepare for deep dive. Take her down to 210 feet [64 m]'; she was diving at 5 degrees. As if from miles away the voice of the communications rating came over, 'Skylark, this is Thresher. Starting deep dive.' At 0835, Thresher was at 322 ft (98 m), still going down at a leisurely 11 knots, the dive now at 15 degrees. By 0912 hours the communication rating's voice had become unclear. The cooks aboard Thresher had cleared away the breakfast and normal daily routine was well underway – everything seemed to be going as planned and she was nearly at her trial depth. Suddenly there was a roar from the engine room. A fine jet of sea water was lancing into the boat and within seconds, cables to the nuclear reactor were covered. The damage was not serious, but as a precaution the engineer officer advised closing down the reactor. The propellers were still slowly churning when seconds later the engine room reported the cables mended, but it was too late.

It would take seven minutes to reactivate the nuclear reactor, seven minutes during which the boat would be stationary, without power, bows pointing sharply upwards. Slowly she began to slip downwards, stern first – 0913 hours, Thresher had passed the 1,000-ft (305-m) mark. 'Blow main ballast tanks', ordered the captain. Aboard Skylark they could hear the air being forced into the tanks. Pressurized air rushed into the

A fine head-on view of the ill-fated USS Thresher at sea. The class was continued and at present there are 13 of the type in service.

ballast tanks; the dive slowed down, then stopped; now her positive buoyancy *must* take her up. It seemed an age aboard *Skylark* as the submarine lay poised, then they felt she was slowly, horribly slowly, slipping backwards. At 0917 hours they indistinctly heard the captain's voice over the telephone, 'We're past trial depth' – there was a frightful noise – then silence. The *Thresher* had broken up, imploding under the enormous water pressure. Death and destruction were instantaneous as great chunks of metal, all that remained of *Thresher*, drifted silently to settle on the bottom, over 4,000 ft (1,200 m) below the surface. So in less than five minutes the most advanced nuclear submarine the world had ever known had disintegrated.

When the bathyscaphe *Trieste* went down all she could find to photograph were great pieces of metal widely scattered over the sea bed. All that was brought to the surface was a piece of metal 56 in (142 cm) long, '593 boat' – *Thresher*'s number. A terrible lesson had been learned, one which threw the U.S. submarine command into a near panic: the buoyancy tanks aboard nuclear submarines must be enlarged, a contention that had been held by a number of submariners before the disaster.

The United States Navy, and by now the Soviet Navy, had a 'true' submarine. What was required now was a devastating weapon with which to arm it, one that

The 'Swiftsure' class, HMS Splendid, *commissioned in 1981, as she blows her tanks. With five different sonar rigs, she is well able to hunt and destroy enemy submarines if the need arises.*

would become the most powerful weapon – the answer was, of course, the Polaris IRBM (Intermediate Range Ballistic Missile).

Until a countermeasure or sensor is found – both the Soviets and the West see this as one of their most important, if not *the* most important, scientific research programme – the Polaris submarine lying on the sea bed, on station, its nuclear missiles ready for instant firing, remains undetectable. However, the modern diesel-electric submarine has a number of advantages over the nuclear boat: it is extremely quiet and can work in much shallower water than its nuclear counterpart. The largest diesel-electrics are in the 2,500-tonne range

while the only nuclear submarine in this range is the French 'Rubis' class. A new generation of diesel-electric ocean-going submarines is just starting to come into service with types like the TR 1700, built by Thyssen Nordseewerke GmbH and now in service, and the Type 2400, which is being built by Vickers U.K. to replace the Royal Navy's 'Oberon' class.

The major advantage enjoyed by the nuclear submarine is its ability to travel for much longer periods at high speed, a feature required by navies that have to operate across oceans. In the event of an ultimate war, the navies of the democracies and those of the Soviets could once again become the most telling single factors.

Overleaf: An artist's impression of the Royal Navy's 'Trident' class submarine to be built by Vickers. They are due to enter service in the mid-1990s and will carry Trident D5 missiles, each with 13 MIRV warheads and a range of 6,000 miles (9,600 km).

THE CHANGING BALANCE OF SEA POWER

The uneasy alliance between the western Allies and the Soviet Union during the Second World War broke into open hostility at its end. Each eyed the other with almost obsessive suspicion and, as the 'cold war' progressed, as potential aggressors. The ideological gulf between western capitalism and the communism of the Soviet Union and her satellites was too wide to bridge and yet another arms race began. At first both camps had their hands full trying to repair the ravages of war; the Soviet Union had suffered an estimated 20 million casualties and her western territories were devastated; Great Britain's mercantile

marine had almost been annihilated. To meet the needs of peace, men had to be demobilized, displaced persons housed and fed, enemy countries policed and administered. Navies turned their attention to clearing minefields, salvaging wrecks and generally clearing the debris of war. Many warships went into reserve; others were put in mothballs or scrapped. Once the euphoria of peace had worn off and the work of rehabilitation got well underway, maritime countries turned their attention to formulating a naval policy, one most likely to counter any future Soviet threat.

With the U-Boat campaign still very

much in mind, those island countries, which by necessity regarded the sea as their primary means of communication, sought ways of ensuring an uninterrupted flow of vital imports. With the possible exception of the Soviet Union – which is, to all intents and purposes, self-sufficient in raw materials – most countries are islands or have a large seaboard to protect and need to import to exist. A satisfactory maritime policy calls for a total integration of all sea-going activities and back-up facilities necessary to ensure that all operate efficiently. This implies the need not only for an adequate mercantile marine and a navy sufficiently strong to protect it, but for the many facilities and services that go to maintaining them: shipyards, docks, customs, navigation services, repair facilities, naval policing and many other activities essential to a maritime nation.

Two major naval changes emerged from the Second World War: firstly, the final ousting of the big-gun battleship as the capital ship, a role now performed by the aircraft carrier; and secondly, a dramatic alteration in world sea power. No longer was Great Britain the mistress of the oceans; the enormous United States Navy,

the most powerful in history, had taken on that role and the Royal Navy had become a poor second. The 123 aircraft carriers and 41,000 naval aircraft alone gave the United States a mastery of the seas that no other country could begin to challenge. Yet basing naval power on an aircraft-carrier fleet had a number of drawbacks, not the least of which was the cost of replacement. As costs rocketed, the second generation of nuclear-powered carriers each topped the $2 billion mark; even the United States with its vast defence budget was forced to draw in its horns. In times of war political parties within a democracy are more or less in agreement and support limitless spending to achieve victory, but this is not so in times of peace, when politicians use defence budgets to gain political clout, often to the detriment of the armed forces.

The Soviet Navy emerged from the war with a strength in European waters of three battleships, nine cruisers, 75 destroyers and 157 submarines, but her wartime record at sea had been abysmal. In all the Soviet Navy only managed to sink 445,526 tons (452,654 tonnes) of merchant shipping and 114 warships (63,255 tons/64,267 tonnes), and most of this success came when the Nazi war machine was in decline not in 1941 and 1942 when it was needed. It could not hope to compete with the United States Navy and decided to concentrate on a coastal defence fleet, consisting of small, fast surface craft, land-based bombers and, above all, submarines.

Geographically sea power has never played more than a minor part in Russian strategy, though her expansion under Peter the Great pushed the borders to the Sea of Azov and the Baltic and under Catherine the Great southwards to the Black Sea. Basically the country is land-locked with long frontiers, so it has always been Russian armies that have played the major part in the country's defence and foreign policy. Sea power could have little significance to a country with a small mercantile marine, few overseas commitments and only a handful of ports and cities vulnerable to seaborne assault. Yet the U.S.S.R.'s coastline stretches 28,000 miles (44,800 km), albeit 90 per cent of it ice-bound, and under the Czars, the navy was among the top six in size. A further problem was that any Russian fleet had to be split to cover four main areas: the Baltic, the White and Black Seas and the Pacific.

USS Philippine Sea *refuels from USS* Platte. *The destroyer USS* Watts *is also being refuelled while operating with the 7th Fleet in 1955.*

The Soviet Union has half a million officers and men in its navy. Under the leadership of Admiral S.G. Gorshkoy, the Soviet Navy is now second only to the U.S.A. in the size of its fleet.

Despite her overwhelming land commitments, Russia has always had a persistent desire to operate a 'blue ocean' fleet for prestige reasons, but caution and cost has tempered this desire; one school of Russian naval thought had traditionally insisted on a coastal defence force only. This vacillation has persisted down the years and it is only in recent times that a comprehensive naval policy has been formulated. The 'Old School' of thought maintained that the Soviet Union should have a balanced fleet for the 'open ocean' with battleships as its backbone, backed up by cruisers, destroyers, submarines and aircraft. This was violently opposed by the 'Young School', who insisted that the Soviet Union should not be hampered by conventional naval strategy, but should adopt a policy specifically designed for the requirements of the U.S.S.R., combining an all-arms approach that would avoid a 'Jutland' confrontation. 'Young School' adherents demanded that 'command of the sea' should be strived for only in those areas that affected the defence of the 'homeland', in effect, light coastal defence craft, shore-based naval aircraft and coastal defences, with a pre-

ponderance of submarines. A. M. Yakimychev, a leading figure in the 'Young School', bitterly attacked the notion of a 'small (weak) fleet' with its insistence on the big ship, as playing into the hands of potential enemies, 'We must find ways and other means of waging war at sea with our potential enemies.'

The navy passed through troubled times between 1917 and 1922. Always treated with suspicion by ideological and political enemies within the Soviet Union because of its high proportion of Czarist officers – politically unreliable class enemies – the navy was purged after Kronstadt. The unsuccessful mutiny of the Baltic fleet in 1922, a rising against the increasing autocracy of the Lenin regime, was followed by a blood bath, mass executions and deportations to Siberia. The 'naval forces of the workers', however, began to win back ground in 1928 with an expanded shipbuilding programme in the first Five Year Plan. By 1941, the year of the German invasion, the Soviet Union could boast more than 500 warships, including the biggest submarine fleet in the world. Numerically the Soviet Navy was strong, but in quality of both ships and personnel it was weak.

In 1938 Stalin had established the 'Soviet Navy', an independent command, and despite opposition he demanded a fleet for the 'open ocean', which seemed to have very little strategic value, merely a political one. It is of some significance that Stalin liked to go aboard big ships at every opportunity, holding receptions and dinners aboard them. Whatever Stalin planned, the Soviet fleet at the outbreak of war with Germany had been supplemented only with light coastal craft and submarines.

Stalin resumed his 'fleet for the open ocean policy' in 1946, continuing a massive shipbuilding programme, while con-signing the 'fleet in being' to the role of 'fortress fleet' to protect the Soviet Union from an amphibious invasion. A 20-year construction programme was initiated, scheduled to build 40 cruisers, 210 destroyers, 180 escorts, a staggering 1,200 submarines and four aircraft carriers. This policy was questioned later by Admiral Gorshkov, who pointed out that it was absurd to assume that a potential enemy strike would occur solely in coastal waters, when potential enemy carrier-based aircraft could mount an attack on Soviet naval bases from a distance. After 1953 the Stalinist shipbuilding programme was reviewed and the building of cruisers and medium-sized submarines and the proposed

A Soviet 'Foxtrot' class diesel-electric submarine on exercise with a 'Kashin' class guided-missile destroyer. The 'Kashin' class was the first warship class designed with an all-gas turbine propulsion system.

An Egyptian 'Osa' class missile boat, armed with four Styx surface-to-surface missiles. It was this type of missile which sank an Israeli destroyer.

four aircraft carriers was abandoned. 'Zulu' class submarines were converted to missile carriers and 'Golf' class submarines were especially constructed to carry surface-to-surface missiles. The value of the SS.N.2 Styx, which could be carried in very small craft, was demonstrated when the Israeli conventional destroyer *Eliat* was sunk by missiles fired by an Egyptian fast patrol boat when still lying in harbour. Out of four Styx fired, three scored hits – the fourth failed to do so because the *Eliat* had

already gone down by the time it arrived.

Between 1961 and 1962, with the appearance of American naval aircraft with a considerably longer range and the extensive threat of Polaris submarines, the optimistic Soviet programme was seen to be totally inadequate. American carrier aircraft, operating from the South Norwegian Sea, now had the range to strike deep into the U.S.S.R, and Polaris submarines could deliver their missiles to anywhere in the central U.S.S.R., from numerous points

along the 28,000-mile (44,800-km) sea-board. To meet a carrier threat, Soviet cruisers would have to steam over 400 miles (640 km) to make contact with the enemy in the South Norwegian Sea, running the gauntlet of air and missile attack that could lead only to certain destruction. American carrier-strike forces had to be destroyed before they reached their aircraft launching zones, while the Soviet anti-carrier forces would have to overcome growing multi-defence systems: anti-ship, anti-aircraft and anti-submarine, particularly the developing American underwater detection system, designed to inhibit the Soviet strategic submarine operational potential.

This despair caused a hasty reappraisal of Soviet naval and shipbuilding programmes. Under Admiral Gorshkov, now commander-in-chief of the Soviet Navy, a fast, startlingly new concept began to take shape. The advent of the 16-tube Polaris submarine underlined just how far the Soviets had lagged behind. Gorshkov oversaw the dismantling of the older battleships and cruisers, and instituted the new building programme, but he fought diligently to retain surface ships, despite Krushchev's belief that only coastal defences were relevant. Gorshkov was able to sway the government to retain surface ships by arguing that although they were not as important as they had once been, they still had an important enough role to play, particularly in view of the NATO carrier force. The number of surface-to-surface missiles was cut by half, to be replaced by anti-submarine and anti-aircraft defences. 'J' class diesel-powered submarines gave way to 'E' class nuclear-powered vessels. The range of operation of the Soviet Navy had begun to go beyond her coastal waters.

Surface ships, coastal boats and sub-marines were armed with cruise missiles, comparable to the American Regulus, as were the Tupolev Tu-16, *Badger* bombers – their primary target was the aircraft carrier. During the 1960s the Soviet Union attempted to influence world events by arming Third World countries with cruise and ballistic missiles, and a number of 'brush fire' wars broke out. Israel, learning from the *Eliat* disaster, turned from conventional surface craft to a fleet of small, fast missile ships, firing Israeli-developed missiles. They were used to great effect in the Yom Kippur War of 1973. This, the first direct encounter between two missile-armed fleets, ended in the destruction of 13 Egyptian and Syrian missile boats, whereas the Israeli fleet did not lose a single ship. This victory demonstrated the value of combining a successful tactical missile attack with efficient countermeasures: defensive missiles to take out the incoming enemy missiles; reducing the radar and heat emanating from a ship, towards which a missile can be homed; by diverting it by means of 'chaff' and jamming enemy radar.

Like it or not, the Soviet Navy had been dragged into an 'ocean theatre' of operations rather than a coastal, 'internal seas' one, by the advent of the Polaris submarines and the need for anti-submarine warfare (ASW) techniques. By the mid-1960s Gorshkov was winning his way and the Soviet Navy was beginning to take on a more balanced, powerful look. By 1963 the Soviet fleet was beginning to formulate its new 'strategic mission': to use sea space, to extend its countermeasures to within missile range of potentially hostile carriers, to push out its maritime frontiers. One aspect of this new strategy was the use of helicopters for ASW. This meant that helicopters also must put to sea in some force, which brought about the introduction of the 'anti-submarine cruisers', the *Moskva* and *Leningrad*, fast – 30 knot plus – 15,000 tonners; each carried 18 helicopters as well as a wide range of missile armament. To these were later added two more spec-

tacular developments, the 'Kirov' and 'Kiev' classes.

The *Kiev*, one of four, is a 43,000-ton (43,700-tonne) carrier with a 600-ft (183-m) angled flight-deck and a speed of 30 knots plus. Her air group consists of 24 helicopters and 12 V/STOL Yak-36 *Forgers*, the equivalent of the Hawker Sea Harrier. Her missile armament is far beyond the range of any Western carriers, almost that of a missile cruiser. The 'Kirov' cruiser may be assumed to be, in the first instance, a protective escort for the 'Kiev' class carriers. As it is proposed that in future they will be nuclear-powered, they can be regarded only as ocean-going ships, operating beyond the Baltic and Black Seas. These 30,000-ton (30,480-tonne) ships, with their wide range of missiles, ASW and anti-missile countermeasures, are probably the most powerful and deadly warships afloat.

The naval arms race still goes on today,

A Kamov KA-25 anti-submarine helicopter hovers alongside the Moskva, a helicopter cruiser. The 'Moskva' class was due to number 20 vessels but its poor sea-keeping qualities led to only the Moskva and Leningrad being built.

Designing vessels required large numbers of highly trained draughtsmen to draw up thousands of detailed drawings. It was a long and expensive operation.

with the Soviet Navy taking the lead, especially in the submarine sector; it is believed that the Soviet Navy has well over 100 missile-armed nuclear submarines, with about 66 fitted to fire ballistic missiles, as well as a huge fleet of non-nuclear submarines.

Modern Warship Design

In the days of the battleship the naval architect had to compromise between speed, hitting power and armour; since 1945 his areas of compromise have changed dramatically but, nevertheless, they still exist. Since the end of the war, naval tactics and technology have undergone a revolution brought about by the introduction of modern electronics and its effect on weaponry. With increased weapon speed and range the need for fast surface vessels has declined and modern ships on the whole are slower than their Second World War counterparts (this applies particularly to destroyers, frigates and escort vessels).

The whole concept of naval tactics has altered. Not all ships within a task force are necessarily combatants. Some have a purely defensive role protecting the combatants – usually aircraft carriers – from missile and submarine attack; others act as communication and radar ships for the fleet, for today one ship is capable of

Computers have now become an important tool in the design of modern ships. Here a draughtsman uses a CAD/CAM computer to draw up a new plan. The computer allows him to see what would happen all the way through the plans if he was to change anything.

acting as another ship's radar platform.

In a peacetime environment, rocketing costs have imposed a thankless task on the naval architect: how to get the maximum amount of firepower and protection for the least amount of money – and electronics are by far the most costly part of a ship's make-up. By the late 1960s steel had become the least expensive item, and electronic control of a weapon often proved more costly than the weapon itself. The vast number of vessels used in the Pacific theatre during the Second World War are a thing of the past, but with the reduction in numbers, the value of each ship correspondingly increases, and with it the need for the greatest overall protection. Strike weapons have developed side by side with countermeasures, and ships, although generally having an overall 'strike' capacity, usually have a specialist element – ASW, anti-aircraft defence, surface-to-surface attack or minesweeping.

Weapons Systems

The rise of the self-propelled missile has led to fundamental changes in naval tactics and the design of ships. Missiles have, in the main, replaced the gun as a primary weapon. However, in the case of the gun, the weapon itself is expensive and its projectile relatively cheap, but the opposite is true of the cruise missile – it is the missile itself that is expensive and its launcher relatively cheap. The range of many missiles is greater than that of any gun, and in an action where very few rounds are required – most modern ships can take only one or two hits – cruise missiles give small craft, destroyers and frigates, a greater hitting power than Second World War battleships. This, together with cost, has led navies to adopt missile weapon systems in smaller, less vulnerable craft.

Of course, cruise missiles are also decidedly more accurate. Gunnery, even the most efficiently controlled, could expect only 10 per cent accuracy. On the other hand, claims for missiles such as Talos and Exocet are as high as 75 per cent hits. A missile-armed cruiser carrying up to 100 missiles can do a lot of damage to an enemy. Even smaller cruise missiles, such as the Harpoon, can carry explosive power equivalent to a 10-in shell, over 60 miles (96 km) with radar terminal accuracy at the end of its flight. However, the missile has to penetrate growing defensive barriers and avoid anti-missile weapons and diversionary systems.

One such diversionary tactic is the use of chaff as an electronic countermeasure. Chaff acts as a decoy system that affects the performance of radar-guided missiles, offering them an alternative target. Chaff consists of strips of metal foil which can be fired to form a cloud. It is almost always known when an enemy force is within missile range (although there were instances during the Falklands Campaign when this was not the case and which ended in disaster) and chaff can be fired at long range by shell or rocket or even dropped from an aircraft. The cloud formed confuses enemy radar giving a false position for the target. If a missile is on its way, a chaff cloud fired a mile or so from the ship will decoy the missile away from its target by influencing the radar in the nose of the missile. Should, however, the missile's radar be firmly locked onto the target, a ship can create a large chaff cloud between itself and the missile. This causes the missile to home in on the centre of the combined chaff and ship echo, which, given sufficient time, allows the ship to manoeuvre out of danger.

In the past ships were designed around their most powerful weapon; for instance the between-wars' naval conferences laid

A British sailor loads a Plessey anti-ship missile decoy. When the decoy is fired, it creates a cloud of very fine metal chaff which the incoming missile will home onto instead of the ship.

down the size of a battleship's guns, and naval architects designed the ship around that. Today's ships are designed for a purpose and weapons are selected to carry out that purpose – ASW, anti-aircraft defence or surface warfare. For instance a ship given an ASW role would primarily be equipped with anti-submarine weaponry and helicopters, with secondary back-up of anti-aircraft weaponry and so on. In the past a ship had more weapon systems – main armaments, secondary armaments, AA guns, torpedoes and depth-charges – all of which operated independently, so a ship could still fight on, as one after another of its weapons was eliminated. This is not necessarily the case with modern frigates and destroyers. For example, radar, which must be placed high in the ship, can be put out of action if its wave guides are destroyed by flying fragments and this renders any radar-guided missiles useless. There is also a strong possibility that the launcher might simply jam, or the electronics malfunction – both of these problems have been experienced in action. One ship during the Falklands Campaign was made virtually useless (but for a Second World War Oerlikon), when an aircraft cannon shell penetrated its central electronic core. One lesson that came out of the Falklands action was that the Type 22

frigate really needed an automatic computer-controlled 4.5-in gun as well as its missile weaponry, particularly for its ground-support role ashore, where a large number of shells were required to be delivered over a wide area. A further problem to the weapon-system concept is the ever-changing complexity and sophistication of the missiles themselves.

Air Defence

A ship primarily designed for anti-aircraft warfare (for example, a 'goal-keeping' role in relationship to an aircraft carrier) has two changing targets: the aircraft itself and the missile it releases. Presuming that the aircraft intends to release its missile beyond gun range, the first task of a ship's surface-to-air missile (SAM) is to take the aircraft out before it can release its missile; failing that, the ship's missile must change its target to the much smaller aircraft missile. Unfortunately SAM systems have a maximum raid-handling ability, and too large an attack by too many aircraft can saturate an anti-aircraft defence system allowing missiles and bombs to get through to their target. This would be particularly disastrous in the case of a nuclear warhead, where a near miss is more than sufficient to take out a target.

A 'County' class cruiser underway. It is armed with Exocet anti-ship missiles, Seaslug and Sea Cat anti-aircraft missiles and two 4.5-in guns.

The Destroyer

In recent years the difference between destroyers and frigates has become confusing, as one overlaps the other in size, sometimes reaching the displacement of a Second World War light cruiser. But the Royal Navy insists on retaining the nomenclature and, by and large, destroyers have an anti-aircraft defence role, whereas frigates have a general-purpose or anti-submarine role. As the era of the converted missile cruiser was phased out, destroyers and frigates, which were growing larger, became the main missile ships of a fleet, and were tailored for specific roles.

The first destroyers to be designed primarily for an air-defence role came into being between 1963 and 1970. These were the 5,440-ton (5,530-tonne) 'County' class ships, one of the most elegant classes of ships ever designed. As big as a light cruiser, they were powered by two steam turbines and four gas turbines, which, geared to the same shaft, allow for speeds up to 30 knots, 25 knots on steam. Gas-turbine boost assists a rapid acceleration. Each of her twin shafts driving two five-bladed propellers has a combined output of 15,000 shp from the steam turbines plus 7,500 shp from each of two gas turbines.

The 'County' class also carry four Exocet surface-to-surface missiles for anti-ship attack, each of which has to be pointed to within 30 degrees of the target before being launched from its single cell. From then on the missile's inertial guidance takes over, bringing the weapon onto target. This Exocet battery replaced 'B' turret, one of four 4.5-in automatic guns, with which the 'County' class was originally fitted. The missile itself skims the surface of the sea controlled by a radio-altimeter linked to its controls, making it difficult for enemy radar to pick it up; once within radar distance of the target, its active radar system switches on and it homes in on the enemy ship. As witnessed in the Falklands, this weapon has good resistance to electronic counter-measures and its 352-lb (160-kg) warhead is highly destructive, although the 93 per cent accuracy claimed for it was more than optimistic.

For close-in air defence, there are two quadruple Sea Cat launchers. Propelled by a two-stage solid propellant rocket motor, the Sea Cat is a very manoeuvrable close-range weapon system, controlled by two

Port quarter view of the Soviet 'Sovremenny' class destroyer Otlichnny, underway in 1985. Note the vast range of radars. The class came into service in 1982. Among her weapons are two new types of missiles: the SS-N-22 surface-to-surface missile and the surface-to-air SA-N-7 system.

men in a director unit. 'County' class ships have two triple torpedo-tubes for anti-submarine defence, fly a Wessex 3 anti-submarine helicopter and have a full range of sensors, a medium-range sonar, air warning radar, target indicator radar and height-finding radar. This versatile class of ship had its baptism of fire during the Falklands Campaign where she proved herself both in attack and defence. 'County' class destroyers carry a ship's company of 485.

The American equivalent of the 'County' class missile destroyer is the 6,210-ton (6,310-tonne) 'Kidd' class destroyer, although coming in as the 'County' class are being phased out; the first of the 'Kidd' class was launched in 1979. Although carrying anti-submarine weapons systems, they are optimized as general warfare vessels, carrying eight Harpoon surface-to-surface anti-shipping missiles, the Asroc ASW missiles, and are the most powerful destroyers in the U.S. Navy. The four ships of the class were ordered by Iran but were taken over by the Navy after the fall of the Shah. The basic design is that of the 'Spruance' class. Originally it had been intended that the anti-submarine 'Spruance' class would be built to the same standard as that of the 'Kidd' class but it was considered to be too expensive.

Even later than the U.S. 'Kidd' class, the Soviet 'Sovremenny' class – the first one was commissioned in 1980 – is a workmanlike destroyer designed principally for surface warfare, probably in conjunction with the larger, 8,500-ton (8,640-tonne) 'Udaloy' class.

USS Kidd	
Displacement	6,210 tons (6,310 tonnes)
Length	563 ft (172 m)
Missiles	8 Harpoons in quadruple canister launchers
	1 Asroc ASW
Guns	2 5-in
AS Weapons	2 triple Mk 32 torpedo tubes (anti-submarine homing torpedoes)
Aircraft	2 helicopters
Speed	33 knots
Ship's company	338

Sovremenny	
Displacement	6,000 tons (6,100 tonnes)
Length	511 ft (156 m)
Missiles	8 SS.N.22 surface-to-surface missiles with a range of 120 nautical miles, in quadruple launchers
	2 SA.N.7 surface-to-air missiles
Guns	4 5-in fully automatic
Aircraft	1 Helix Helicopter
Speed	35 knots
Ship's company	400

HMS Liverpool, a 'Sheffield' class (Type 42) guided-missile destroyer.

Only one Type 82 'Bristol' class destroyer was built. It was designed as an air-defence escort to a new class of fixed-wing aircraft carrier. When this did not materialize, the Type 82 was scrapped and replaced by the smaller, more versatile, 'Sheffield' class. The *Sheffield*, launched in 1973, was the leader of her class and was the first to go down at the Falklands. The 3,500-ton (3,560-tonne) destroyer, Type 42, is a highly successful design, created to carry out all of the tasks of the Type 82, but with only two-thirds of the crew, 253, a considerable saving in technically-skilled personnel. Her principal role is to provide area air defence for a task force, particularly anti-submarine command carriers such as the *Invincible*. The engines, two Rolls-Royce Olympus gas turbines generating 56,000 shp and two Rolls-Royce Tyne gas turbines for cruising, develop a speed of 29 to 30 knots. This allows fierce acceleration to be complemented with economical cruising speeds. The *Birmingham* of this class cost £30,900,000 when she was commissioned in 1976; the *Exeter*, £60,100,000 in 1980; and the latest scheduled ship, somewhere between £78.5 and £80 million.

They are armed with a Sea Dart weapon system, a later generation of surface-to-air missiles, which can take out both aircraft and missile targets. The Sea Dart's Rolls-Royce Odin ramjet gives it supersonic speeds and its high-explosive warhead is effective at both low and high altitudes; it can also be used as a surface-to-surface weapon against ships. Fired from a twin launcher, it has an all-the-way guidance system utilizing a surveillance radar, and one of two twin tracking/illuminating radars in the ship; target selection and data handling is accomplished by computer. This extremely versatile weapon system with its fast-loading capability can offer effective area air cover for ships other than itself.

The 'Sheffield' class also carries a fully automatic Mark 8 4.5-in gun, intended to provide further anti-aircraft fire as well as shore-bombardment support and surface action. In addition she flies a Mark 2 Lynx helicopter for anti-submarine warfare, attack against light craft on the surface, and reconnaissance. For surface attack the Lynx is armed with air-to-surface Sea Skua missiles and Mark 44 torpedoes for anti-submarine attack. Further AS weapons aboard include two triple torpedo tubes firing lightweight Mark 46 homing torpedoes, located by the ship's own radar.

'Forrest' class	
Displacement	4,150 tons (4,220 tonnes)
Length	418 ft (127 m)
Missiles	SAM Tartar (warhead: high explosive; launch weight: 1,500 lb [680 kg]; speed: above Mach 2) fired from a single launcher
Gun	1 5-in automatic
AS Weapons	1 Asroc 8-tube launcher 2 triple torpedo tubes for lightweight Mark 32
Speed	31 knots
Ship's company	337 to 364

'Kanin' class	
Displacement	3,700 tons (3,760 tonnes)
Length	456 ft (139 m)
Missiles	SAM 2 SA.N. 1 twin launcher – close range surface-to-air missiles
Guns	8 57 mm
AS Weapons	3 12-barrelled RBU 6,000 (anti-submarine rockets)
Torpedoes	10 21-in torpedoes
Aircraft	1 helicopter
Speed	34 knots
Ship's company	350

A Soviet 'Kanin' class destroyer makes smoke. 'Kanin' class ships were modified from eight 'Krupny' class anti-ship destroyers. Their role now is anti-aircraft with a secondary anti-submarine role.

This 392-ft (120-m) 3,500-ton (3,560-tonne) class of destroyer with a crew of 280 has a number of counterparts in the United States and Soviet navies. The American 'Forrest' class, although a heavier ship, carries a similar missile armament to the 'Sheffield', as do the considerably heavier 'Coontz' and lighter 'Charles F. Adams' classes.

The Soviets have several similar classes, among them the 'Kanin' and 'Kotlin', which at 2,850 tons (2,900 tonnes) is a lighter craft than 'Sheffield'.

Frigates

Once considered the reconnaissance and fast raiders of a fleet in the days of sail, frigates again came into their own during the Second World War as convoy escort vessels and anti-submarine craft. After 1945 they continued, by and large, their anti-submarine role, but in size they became confused with destroyers although, in the main, they have a slimmer hull. The early *Rothesay* and *Whitby* anti-submarine frigates developed into the 'Leander' class, hard-hitting ships armed originally with twin 4.5-in automatic guns, but later modified to take Ikara and Exocet missiles. Equipped to perform a general-purpose role, they are capable of engaging ships, aircraft and shore targets as well as undertaking their principal role of submarine detection and destruction.

Displacing 2,450 tons (2,490 tonnes), 360 ft (110 m) long, the 'Leander' class are powered by two controlled super-heated boilers and two sets of steam turbines, generating 30,000 shp to give speeds in

The handsome lines of a Soviet 'Krivak' frigate, underway. The launcher for the SS-N-14 retracts for stowage and reloading and rises only just before firing.

excess of 30 knots. Excellent in bad weather, they are among the finest sea-keeping ships ever built. The earliest 'Leanders' came into commission in 1972, and the latest, the *Jupiter*, in 1983. As well as their attack systems, SSM and SAM Exocets or ASW Ikaras, the 'Leanders' carry Sea Cat surface-to-air missiles for their own protection. The AS weaponry is completed with two triple lightweight homing torpedo tubes, as well as a Lynx or Wasp helicopter capable of AS attack.

The Americans have a number of frigates of comparable displacement; all are general purpose with a specialized commitment, some ASW, others with an anti-aircraft role. Perhaps one of the closest to

the 'Leander' is the 'Garcia' class missile frigates.

The Soviet 21 'Krivak' is an equivalent, although it probably fills more of a general purpose role. Soviet warships, on the whole, tend to have austere, workmanlike lines, but the *Krivak*, which appeared in 1970, is a handsome-looking ship with sweeping lines and a sharply cut-away bow. Her four gas-turbine engines give her a speed of 32 knots.

Between 1974 and 1978 a new, small, general-purpose frigate was introduced into the Royal Navy. The 2,500-ton (2,540-tonne) 'Amazon' class designed by Vosper Thornycroft and Yarrow – the first custom-built warship constructed by a commercial

'Garcia' class	
Displacement	2,620 tons (2,660 tonnes)
Length	414 ft (126 m)
Missiles	1 Asroc 8-tube launcher (the rocket-motored missile carries either a depth-charge or homing torpedo dropped by parachute)
Guns	2 5-in automatic
AS Weapons	2 triple torpedo tubes – Mark 32
Aircraft	1 LAMPS (Light Airborne Multi-Purpose Systems) helicopters
Speed	27.5 knots
Ship's company	239–47

'Krivak' class	
Displacement	3,000 tons (3,050 tonnes)
Length	405 ft (123 m)
Missiles	AS 4 SS.N.14 in a quadruple launcher (A winged AS missile based round a homing torpedo or depth-charge) SAM,4 SA.N.4 fired from twin launchers (surface-to-air missiles)
Guns	4 3-in
AS Weapons	2 12 barrelled RBU 6000
Torpedoes	8 21-in in quadruple tubes
Speed	32 knots
Ship's company	220

firm for years – has all the racy lines associated with this firm of shipbuilders.

More like a yacht than a conventional frigate, it sweeps back from prow to stern in

A Royal Navy Type 21 frigate in heavy seas. It was the first R.N. warship to be designed by a commercial shipbuilder for many years.

a graceful line, with a large raked funnel. Nevertheless, it is a hard-hitting, general-purpose ship that proved its worth at the Falklands. With a length of 384 ft (117 m) it carries a ship's company of 175.

These Type 21s are powered by two Rolls-Royce Olympic engines which give 56,000 shp, allowing a startling acceleration to 30 knots, and two Rolls-Royce Tyne gas turbines for cruising, each of 8,500 shp. She is armed with a Mark 8 4.5-in rapid-fire, fully automatic gun.

'Amazon' was designed to protect convoys and other naval craft from attack by surface ships and submarines, using Exocet surface-to-surface missiles and homing torpedoes, fired from two triple torpedo tubes on the upper deck. One quadruple launcher firing Sea Cat SAM missiles supplies her defence against air attack, missiles or fast patrol boats. Her automatic gun can supplement her air defence, take on light surface craft, or be used for shore bombardment. She also carries a Westland Lynx multi-purpose helicopter which, in its anti-submarine role, is capable of carrying either six air-to-surface guided missiles, Sea Skuas or two anti-submarine homing torpedoes.

'Amazon' has a fully computerized 'hands-off' weapon system, sophisticated information equipment and a centralized store-room complex that can supply any

necessary replacement parts by vertical hoist. The highly automated aspects of the ship have allowed the crew to be reduced to 175, which allows more space for accommodation. Naval personnel of the last generation would be astonished at the sight of the ship's facilities; separate dining halls for both senior and junior ratings, a laundry, a sick bay and comprehensive recreational facilities: television, video, radio, cinema and a library.

The Americans have nothing as elegant-looking as the 'Amazon' frigates; their nearest in performance is probably the 'Knox' class.

Opposite: HMS Beaver (Type 22/batch 2) with her Lynx Mk2 anti-submarine helicopter. The batch 2 vessels are 20 ft (6 m) longer than the first five of the class.

'Knox' class	
Displacement	3,011 tons (3,060 tonnes)
Length	438 ft (130 m)
Missiles	SSM – 8 Harpoons in quadruple launchers
	SAM – 1 Sea Sparrow in a multiple launcher (a close-range surface-to-air or surface-to-surface missile)
Gun	1 5-in automatic
AS Weapons	1 Asroc 8-tube launcher
	4 fixed torpedo tubes – Mark 32
Aircraft	1 SH.2 Light Airborne Multi-Purpose Systems helicopter
Speed	27 knots
Ship's company	283

The Soviet Navy has a similar-looking, though much smaller, class to the 'Amazon', but the 'Grisha' class does not quite achieve the 'Amazon's sleek, racy lines.

The Type 22 frigate, the 'Broadsword' class, represented a 'first' for the Royal Navy; she was the first to be built with an all-missile armament – this was later to prove a drawback in action. Originally designed as a successor to the 'Leander' class when the scheduled programme of 26

of that class had been completed, the *Broadsword* and her sister ships turned into extremely powerful submarine-hunters with an effective role to play against surface units. This 410-ft (125-m) long frigate displaces 3,500 tons (3,560 tonnes) and is armed to play both a defensive and attacking role.

She too is an all gas-turbine ship, generating 56,000 shp from two Rolls-Royce Olympus engines, and 8,500 shp from each of two Rolls-Royce Tyne engines, to give a top speed of 30 knots under acceleration, while able to cruise at 18 knots on the Tynes alone. One feature of *Broadsword* is her good sea-keeping; she is easy to handle in the heaviest seas. One of this class on the way to South Georgia in the Falklands was able to plough through mountainous seas at speed, suffering very little superficial damage, while her stabilizers minimized the rolling.

For air defence, her own as well as that

A Soviet 'Grisha' class anti-submarine frigate. The 'Grisha I' and 'Grisha III' classes can be recognized from the KGB operated 'Grisha IIs' by the lack of SA-N-4 missile launchers on the 'Grisha IIs'.

'Grisha' class	
Displacement	950 tons (965 tonnes)
Length	236 ft (72 m)
Missiles	SAM 2 SA.N.4 twin launcher
Guns	2 57-mm twin turret
AS Weapons	2 RBU 6,000
Torpedoes	4 21-in – 2 twin tubes
Speed	30 knots
Ship's company	80
This powerful little ship can also carry up to 18 mines	

The sharp bow of USS Oliver Hazard Perry, silhouetted against the rising sun on the day of her launch. The 'Perry' class is a general-purpose frigate and is in use with the navies of the U.S.A., Australia and Spain.

U.S. technicians monitor displays in the combat information centre aboard the AEGIS guided-missile cruiser USS Ticonderoga. The microchip has led to a revolution in the ways of coping with the threat of high-speed missiles, which are, in their own right, controlled by modern micro-electronics.

of ships being escorted, the class is fitted with Sea Wolf GWS 25 surface-to-air missiles of supersonic speed and great accuracy – it is claimed to have hit a 4.5-in shell and Mach 2 missile targets during firing trials. These missiles are housed in two six-barrelled launchers. These ships did, however, have problems when they first encountered war in the Falkland Islands, but these were ironed out during the campaign. Although the most innovative and advanced system so far, it has one slight flaw: it is a hand-fed system, and handling the 176-lb (80-kg) missile on a slippery deck in a heavy sea has its problems. Nonetheless, its record for taking out Argentinian aircraft sorties was most impressive. The Sea Wolf can also be used as a surface-to-surface missile, but the main SSM system is four Exocets fired from single cells. This class carries no gun and this was found to be a disadvantage during the Falklands Campaign, so now a Mark 8 4.5-in gun has been added to the latest versions. This is another ship that has rocketed in price; *Broadsword*, in 1979, cost £68,600,000; but *Beaver*, in 1984, had nearly doubled to £120 million.

For her main task as a submarine-killer, the Type 22 also carries two Westland Lynx multi-purpose helicopters armed with Sea Skuas and AS torpedoes. The ship is fitted with two triple torpedo tubes firing Mark 46 AS torpedoes. The 'Broadsword' class carries a ship's company of 223.

The Balance of Power

The United States
The vast figure of 123 aircraft carriers that

USS Vincennes, *a 'Ticonderoga' class AEGIS guided-missile cruiser, fires an RUR-5A anti-submarine rocket. The AEGIS system allows the ship automatically to attack targets simultaneously in the air, on the surface and submerged.*

the United States Navy had in commission at the end of the war has now dwindled to 14 operational carriers. Of these, 12 are of postwar construction, including four nuclear-powered vessels but it is still by far the most powerful carrier force in the world today. Three more nuclear carriers are under construction. Each of the carriers in operation has a powerful air wing consisting of 85 to 95 aircraft made up of fighter squadrons, light-attack squadrons, and medium-attack squadrons and capable of immense hitting power when armed with nuclear weapons. There are also squadrons of helicopters for AS and surface warfare, as well as patrol, reconnaissance and early-warning aircraft. The United States Navy's guided-missile cruiser force consists of 28

ships ranging from 4,650 tons (4,720 tonnes) displacement to the 15,540-ton (15,790-tonne) *'Long Beach* nuclear-powered heavy cruiser. There are 35 nuclear-powered ballistic submarines in operation and seven under construction, and four conventionally powered attack submarines. Her guided-missile destroyers number 37, with 32 conventionally gunned destroyers. The U.S. has 40 guided-missile frigates and 59 frigates, backed up by light forces, 63 amphibious assault craft and tank-landing ships, and a force of auxiliary vessels.

The 'Ticonderoga' class guided-missile cruiser is the most important class of vessel to enter service in the U.S. Navy for many years. With its highly sensitive radar system giving all-round cover and AEGIS

Weapons Control it can analyze the threat posed by hundreds of aircraft, missiles, ships and submarines, and then automatically destroy the major targets, either by its own missiles or by those of ships connected by secure data-link. It is the most advanced system in the world; it is also the most expensive. The first USS *Ticonderoga*, was commissioned in 1983 and 33 ships are due to be built.

'Ticonderoga' class				
Displacement	9,600 tons (9.750 tonnes)		2 20-mm Phalanx MK 15 close-in weapon system mountings	
Length	566.8 ft (172.8 m)			
Missiles	2 octuple container-launchers for 16 RGM-84A Harpoon SSM 2 MK 26 twin launchers for up to 68 RIM-67B Standard SAM; later ships: 2 EX41 vertical launchers, 122 assorted missiles; after 1985: 2 vertical launchers, 12 BGM-109 Tomahawk missiles.	Anti-submarine	2 Triple MK 32 tube mounts for 12.75-in MK 46 A/S torpedoes Up to 20 RUR-5A Asroc, part of the total missile strength above and launched from the MK 26 launchers	
		Aircraft	2 Sikorsky SH-60B Seahawk helicopters	
Guns	2 5-in L/54 DP MK 45 single mountings	Speed	30+ knots	
		Ship's crew	350	

'Kirov' class	
Displacement	22,000 tons (22,350 tonnes)
Length	813 ft (248 m)
Missiles	SSM 20 SS.N.19 – range 270 miles (430 km)
	SAM 12 SA.N.6 – with a range of 6 to 40 miles (10 to 64 km), carrying a 200-lb (90-kg) high explosive charge travelling at Mach 6
	SA.N4 surface-to-air missiles
	ASW 2 SS.N.14 – anti-submarine missiles range up to 18 miles (29 km)
Guns	2 5-in
	2 4-in
AS Weapons	1 12-barrelled RBU 6000 – forward
	2 6-barrelled RBU 1000 – aft
Torpedoes	8 21-in in two quadruple tubes
Aircraft	3 Hormone helicopters
Speed	34 knots
Ship's company	900

A Soviet 'Aist' class hovercraft unloads light tanks and naval infantry. They are primarily designed to operate in the Baltic Sea and have a range of up to 350 miles (560 km) at a speed of 65 knots.

The Soviet Union

The Soviet Navy has grown alarmingly since 1970, and can now boast four aircraft carriers, with 17 nuclear carriers under construction, and two helicopter cruisers. There are also two heavily armed battle-cruisers, the *Kirov* and *Baku*, for which the United States has no equivalent. Bristling with sensors and missile launchers, they are the most powerful surface warships afloat today.

The Soviet fleet has 27 missile cruisers and 11 gunned cruisers; 46 guided-missiles destroyers and 24 gunned destroyers; 32 missile frigates and 161 gunned frigates; as well as 28 missile corvettes.

Her light coastal defence consists of 122 missile-carrying fast attack craft and hydrofoils; over 230 fast attack craft and patrol vessels.

The mighty Kirov, *the namesake of the largest class of warship, other than aircraft carriers, built in the last 30 years. Her main armament consists of 20 SS-N-19 vertically launched cruise missiles.*

Most awesome is her extremely powerful submarine fleet. There are 66 nuclear-powered ballistic-missile submarines in commission, 50 nuclear-powered guided-missile submarines, 18 conventional guided-missile submarines, 76 nuclear-powered attack craft and 145 conventional attack submarines.

Great Britain

The Royal Navy pales into insignificance alongside these two mighty fleets with only two AS aircraft carriers, four nuclear-powered ballistic submarines, 12 fleet and 15 patrol submarines. This together with 12 guided-missile destroyers and 44 missile frigates completes the complement.

The Royal Yacht HMS Britannia was originally designed as a medium-sized naval hospital ship. She was pressed into service to help with the evacuation of foreign nationals from Aden in 1986.

SHIPS IN ACTION -THE FALKLANDS CAMPAIGN

The Beginning

On 2 May 1982, in the Atlantic somewhere west of Morocco, the news was broken that Argentinians had invaded the British crown colony of the Falkland Islands. Phase I, weapon training, of the Royal Navy 'Springtrain' (training exercises, held in the spring) had been completed, and the Fleet had sailed from Gibraltar into the Atlantic to continue Phase II of the exercises. The invasion news was greeted with some disbelief and light-hearted banter by many, others took a more serious view of the situation. For a week there had been rumblings from the BBC Overseas Service concerning the Falkland Islands and South Georgia, and some senior officers were furious that the Royal Navy had not already sent a presence to the area. By and large however, there was an air of excitement aboard the ships, almost a holiday spirit; after all, this is what they had been trained for – there was little appreciation of any danger.

Sir Galahad, *manned by the Royal Fleet Auxiliary, leaves her home port on her ill-fated journey 'down south'.*

The survey ship Endurance *in the Antarctic. Her captain had issued many warnings about the Argentinian threat to the Falklands. Her officers and crew were old hands at operating in the dangerous conditions.*

Royal Marines of 3 Commando prepare to board the P & O Canberra for their voyage south. Many of the civilian crew made the same journey. The festive send-off was soon to change as the troops got down to the task of preparing for war.

With the news of the invasion came the signal for the FOFI (Flag Officer First Flotilla), directing him to race south with a spearhead group of eight fast ships. Led by HMS *Glamorgan*, the flagship, were five other destroyers, *Antrim, Glasgow, Coventry, Sheffield* and *Plymouth*, with the Type 22 frigate *Brilliant* and the Type 21 frigate *Arrow* – eight Exocet-armed warships capable of taking out anything afloat or on shore. Each of the ships detailed to head for the Falklands was paired off with a sister ship and gear was transferred by jackstay, boat and vertrep (vertical replenishments by helicopter). Every type of naval and victualling stores were stowed aboard the southbound ships; for 12 hectic hours Sea Wolf missiles, Exocets, 4.5-inch ammunition, machine guns, internal security gear and all manner of electronic and victualling items were transferred. Lynx helicopters flew non-stop in support of their ships, landing cross-deck underslung loads; among the items loaded and landed in this manner were AS torpedoes, as it was likely that submarines would pose a considerable threat to any British task force. As the southbound ships sank lower, the homeward-bound ones rose higher in the water.

David Breen, a civilian Marconi electronics engineer concerned with the development of Sea Wolf missiles, much to his disgust, was disembarked from *Brilliant* and sent home. Later, he persuaded the authorities and his employers to let him rejoin the ship via Ascension, which he did with inestimable benefit to the task force, as he was able to iron out the problems being experienced by the Sea Wolf missiles.

At last the spearhead group turned south for the dreary wastes of the South Atlantic, eight sleek-prowed ships cutting their way at 25 knots through the brilliantly sunlit Atlantic swell. Immediately exercises were begun to hone the crews to battle readiness and, on most ships, hastily prepared presentations with photographs, drawings and maps, as well as naval and military statistics, were put together and broadcast over the ships' closed-circuit TVs. The points emphasized were: why the Falklands were British; what exactly the Argentinians had done; what they were likely to do; the time it would take to get there.

A list of ships' War Orders were immediately put into operation.

1. Identity tags were issued, showing name, official number, religion and blood group – nothing more.

2. Geneva ID cards were to be issued in exchange for Royal Navy ID cards.

3. All gash (ship's waste) from now on was to be burnt, not ditched over the side.

4. Dress at Defence Stations to be AWD carrying lifejackets, survival kit, field dressing and mug.

5. No smoking on upper deck from sunset to sunrise, no smoking at action stations,

controlled smoking at defence stations.

6. Interrogation and prisoner-handling organization to be checked.

7. Resistance to interrogation lecture to be given on CCTV to ensure that ships' companies know what action to take if taken prisoner.

8. All branch badges to be removed.

9. Action stations to be exercised at dawn, 0900 and dusk.

10. Ship to be fully darkened from sunset to sunrise.

11. Paint out Pennant numbers.

12. Classified files to be held permanently in Ship's Office, segregated and ready for ditching in weighted bags.

13. Injectable pain-killing drugs to be issued to First Aid parties, all officers and selected senior ratings.

14. Organization for prisoners of war to be checked.

15. Organization for survivors to be checked.

16. Authority to open fire completely understood.

17. Readiness of equipment and weaponry.

18. Operation room records strictly kept.

19. Emergency Boat Charts kept on bridge.

The ships were ready for war; Operation Corporate was on. Under a hot mid-Atlantic sun the ships' crews continually exercised and drilled for the action that seemed likely to come. The Equator was crossed without ceremony. Extra ammunition was made available and dumps of emergency foodstocks and medical supplies were set up at strategic positions around the ship. By the time the fleet reached Ascension Island it would be battle ready.

In high frequency (HF) radio and radar silence they steamed, 25 to 50 miles (40 to 80 km) apart, south towards Ascension, as the British and Argentinian diplomatic efforts continued to founder and a direct confrontation seemed inevitable. The main Argentinian threat was seen as a surface one and emphasis was placed on surface reporting and over-the-horizon targeting (OTHT) in which helicopters played an important role, acting as the eyes of the task force beyond the range of its radar. In the absence of a carrier, air defence exercises could not be conducted at force level: 'goal-keeping' techniques would have to be approximated until the arrival of the main task force with the carriers *Hermes* and *Invincible*. During the trip to Ascension, the helicopters and the Royal Marines practised attacks against 'Sheffield' class Type 42s, similar to the ones of the Argentine Navy. Inflatable Pacific Seariders, small assault boats, were

An R.N. Lynx lands on HMS Sheffield. *Names and type markings were quickly painted out to prevent enemy eyes from spotting and identifying individual ships.*

The Argentinian submarine Santa Fe, after she had been hit by an AS 12 missile, fired from HMS Plymouth's Wasp helicopter. The Santa Fe had been taking reinforcements to Grytviken.

successfully mounted with Carl Gustav anti-tank weapons, that could skim their rounds into targets at waterline level. The multi-purpose Lynx helicopters made dummy sorties. At the same time, damage-control exercises, weapon firings and plotting exercises were all practised. Lynx aircraft tried every conceivable method of attacking a surface enemy, including strafing with machine guns. (Mounting

machine guns in *Brilliant*'s two Lynxes was one of many successful improvisations made at this time. The metal section of a typist's swivel chair was upturned and bolted to the deck of the helicopter and a brass mounting was constructed to carry a general-purpose machine gun . These were used to great effect on a number of occasions.) In addition to using ESM (Electronic Support Measures), which involves

the detection of targets by listening for radar emissions, helicopters fitted with MAD (Magnetic Anomaly Detectors) trailed their 120-ft (36.5-m) aerial in the water to detect any fluctuations in the earth's magnetic field caused by the hull of a submarine in the water.

On 10 April the spearhead group made Ascension Island, laying off out of sight of land for security reasons. Here the *Antrim,*

Plymouth and *Tidespring,* a fleet tanker, were diverted to South Georgia to give support to the Ice Patrol Ship *Endurance.* There, in Operation Paraquat, they were to land some 60 men, drawn from the S.A.S. (Special Air Service) Regiment to retake the island from the Argentinians. On 14 April *Brilliant*'s commander, Captain John Coward, took a group of ships as far as possible into the South Atlantic towards the Falklands to act as an advance force. His command included the three destroyers, *Coventry*, *Glasgow* and *Sheffield* and the Type 21 frigate *Arrow*. Even as they were heading south, helicopters were vertrepping stores from Ascension to the ships well into the night. Detecting the ships by their 'red head', a group of small flashing red lights at the masthead, was not easy but actually landing the stores in pitch darkness, guided only by a thin horizontal bar of light, on a madly rolling deck, 'goffered' with spray from a mounting sea, was very hazardous indeed.

A gale hit them south of Ascension at 20 degrees latitude. For most it was their first experience of the dreadful seas that can occur in the South Atlantic, where the weather can change dramatically within an hour. For two days ships were lashed by the gale, as they plunged through 30-ft (9-m) high waves smashing over the forecastle.

HMS Arrow, *an 'Amazon' class (Type 21) frigate, was part of the Task Force which Admiral Woodward sent to retake South Georgia.*

The ships' stabilizers helped neutralize the roll, but there was a sickening crash into the trough of each wave. At 40 degrees latitude, on the edge of the 'roaring forties', they began 'box sailing' in gigantic squares, as they waited for *Hermes*, *Invincible* and the rest of the main force to arrive.

On 22 April *Brilliant* was ordered to detach and make for the coast of South Georgia with all possible speed to support the *Antrim* group in Operation Paraquat.

Two of the three Wessex helicopters at their disposal had crashed while attempting to extricate a special force from a glacier, so the two Lynx aircraft aboard *Brilliant* were essential for the successful outcome of the operation. At 2030 hours she set off; turning into the teeth of a full gale she managed 17 knots, smashing through mountainous seas, the urgency of the situation causing her to press on even at the risk of damaging the ship. In the event the only damage she sustained, with waves occasionally breaking over her *bridge*, was a slight buckling on the forescreen aft of the Exocet.

In spite of the heavy seas *Brilliant* joined the *Antrim* group, 150 miles (240 km) north of South Georgia, on 24 April, to find a further complication had arisen. An Argentine submarine, the *Sante Fe,* had been spotted off Grytviken harbour and the hunt was on. At 0855 the remaining Wessex spotted the submarine on the surface, about to dive to take up a patrol position to intercept the British ships. 'Wolf. Wolf.' came clearly over the radio, the signal for 'submarine on the surface', and the Wessex went in with a depth-charge attack. Lynx 341 took off from *Brilliant* to join the attack; ahead she could see *Antrim*'s Wessex hovering above the *Sante Fe,* waiting the Lynx's arrival before returning to her ship to rearm. The submarine's sail appeared to be damaged and she was weeping oil, heading for Cumberland Bay and Grytviken harbour.

The Lynx made a classic torpedo attack, but the captain of the *Sante Fe,* seeing the Mark 46 AS torpedo parachuting down on his starboard side, decided to remain on the surface. With enough high explosive circling below him to blow his boat out of the water – the Mark 46 cannot operate at depths above 30 feet (9 m) – he had no choice but to run for home on the surface. The Lynx's observer scrambled into the back and the helicopter came in for a strafing attack with her machine gun. Although a 7.62-mm bullet would have little effect on the submarine's fin, it caused the crew to scatter, and it was not until the third pass that they began to fire back with their own general-purpose machine gun. The Lynx continued to strafe the *Sante Fe* at a range of 300 ft (90 m) and a height of 30 ft (9 m). Suddenly the Lynx crew saw the trail of an AS 12 wire-guided missile flash past to crash into the fin of the submarine, fired from a Wasp helicopter; the second AS 12 crashed into the water ahead of her. The *Sante Fe* limped into Grytviken and tied up alongside the jetty, obviously in a critical condition and likely to sink at any moment. The SAS landing went ahead only to be halted at 1715 when the Argentinians ran up the white flag.

The next day the *Sante Fe*, with a list to port and down by the head, was slowly sinking. Her fin was riddled with bullets and part of her bridge had been blown away by an AS 12 missile. However, most of these missiles had punched a hole right through before exploding. The inside of the submarine was a shambles, although there was little evidence of this from the outside. It was decided to move her away from the jetty when attempts to restore full buoyancy had failed. Rather than sink her in deep water, an attempt was made to move her to a berth near the old whaling station, where she could gently settle on the bottom. A crew of Argentinians was detailed to man the switchboard in the control room, under an armed guard of Royal Marines to prevent them from attempting to scuttle the boat; her commander, accompanied by Captain Coward, himself a submariner, would direct the operation from the bridge. Constantly blowing tanks, the *Sante Fe* was limping towards her new berth when suddenly she listed violently and began to lose buoyancy. Frantic orders were shouted from the bridge in Spanish; the crew panicked and the one man who kept his head, a petty officer, who rushed to blow the ballast, was shot by a Marine in the belief that he was trying to scuttle the submarine. Despite this tragic incident, the *Sante Fe* was successfully berthed, and Argentinian and British alike hastily scrambled ashore.

On the afternoon of 28 April *Plymouth* and *Brilliant* steamed from South Georgia in thick weather to join the main force off the Falklands, under surveillance from long-range Argentinian reconnaissance aircraft. The *Brilliant* immediately took up her position as 'goal-keeper' to *Invincible*, offering her Sea Wolf air defence against possible attack by Argentinian aircraft delivering bombs or Exocet missiles. An organized system of defence evolved, using a combination of Sea Wolf, Sea Dart, chaff and jammer Lynx. Throughout the night RAS (Refuelling At Sea) had been carried out – cold, miserable operations, further compli-

cated by an enforced zig-zag in case of hostile submarines. For the warships it was a thankless chore experienced every few days; for the Merchant Fleet, storing and fuelling was a continuous, unbroken, bone-chilling series of monotonous operations.

Merchantmen at the Falklands

Operation Corporate would have been totally out of the question without the assist-

ance of the Merchant Navy. Over the years the Royal Navy's commitments had centred around the NATO defence of Europe and other possible operations within reach of home bases or friendly ports; the possibility of fighting a naval war at the bottom of the world had never entered into its calculations. This, coupled with the rundown of surface ships following the government white paper of 1981, 'The Way Forward', made it impossible for the Fleet to mount an operation 8,000

miles (12,800 km) away using only its own ships. Such an amphibious operation against strong opposition, with the nearest friendly base at Ascension Island, was a very tall order indeed.

On 4 April, two days after Argentine troops had landed on the Falklands, Queen Elizabeth II signed the 'Requisitioning of Ships Order 1982' and the Merchant Navy swung into action. The Order, however, was nothing new. The requisitioning of merchant ships in time of war dates back to

The busy flight-deck of HMS Invincible. Her Sea Harriers kept up a regular CAP (Combat Air Patrol) over the main Task Force, while her Sea King helicopters provided essential airlifts.

The ships of the Royal Fleet Auxiliary kept the Task Force supplied. Here Cunard's Queen Elizabeth II *takes on more fuel as she heads south.*

Richard I and the Third Crusade, and at the height of the Armada battle in the Channel, seven merchantmen were pressed into service as fireships at the Calais Roads. In 1982 some merchantmen were chartered, others were requisitioned, mainly to protect owners from contractual disagreements.

No plans had been formulated to meet such a contingency as a confrontation in the South Atlantic; there was no previous experience on which to draw; the whole concept had to be devised from scratch. Every day brought news of the Argentine build-up of equipment and men on the Islands. Enemy strength was eventually estimated at more than 15,000 troops. One of the most urgent priorities in Britain, therefore, was to transport like numbers of troops from the United Kingdom. Ships

had to be chosen with great care having regard for their range, endurance and their likelihood of sea-keeping in the fierce seas of the South Atlantic. The first choice for a troopship soon narrowed itself down to the 44,807-ton (45,525-tonne) *Canberra* and, as early as 9 April, she sailed south in company with the 'Roll-on/Roll-off' ferry the 5,463-ton (5,550-tonne) *Elk.* Aboard were 3,000 crack troops of 3rd Commando Brigade, Royal Marine Commandos and men of the Parachute Regiment. The *Elk* carried the supporting arms and war reserve equipment, ammunition, bridging equipment and eight light tanks, Scimitars and Scorpions. (They were shadowed by a Soviet observation ship as far as Freetown in West Africa.) The two merchant ships were soon followed by the 12,988-ton (13,196-tonne) *Norland,* the 4,190-ton

(4,257-tonne) *Europic* ferry and numerous others. In all, 53 merchantmen were in operation at the Falklands, easily outnumbering the Royal Navy ships engaged.

As the Argentine reinforcement of the Falklands built up, more troops, including the Gurkhas, had to be rushed out from England and the *Queen Elizabeth II* was requisitioned 19 hours before she was due to sail on a Mediterranean cruise. Fitted out with two helicopter decks and over one thousand camp beds, she set sail with 3,000 troops aboard. At first it was intended that the merchantmen should not be exposed to any serious danger of attack, but it soon became obvious that they would be in the thick of it, open to air attack by bombs and missiles.

All the merchant ships chosen had to be modified, the modifications ranging from minor adjustments to quite major structural alterations and additions, but amazingly enough, none of these took more than a few days. Alterations were often designed on the back of envelopes and in some instances decided on the spot, to be carried out immediately as the designer moved on. The *Canberra* was turned into a troopship in two days flat; the P & O liner *Uganda* was converted into a hospital ship in three days. In view of the extremely bad weather and seas likely to be experienced at the Falklands, it was necessary to fit helicopter landing decks as it would be impossible to land men and stores by boat in such seas. Seventeen ships were fitted with helicopter pads, ranging in size from those capable of landing the 46,000-lb (21,000-kg) Chinook to ones able only to take the considerably smaller Wasp helicopter. In the case of the large liners, the swimming pools, designed to take up to 100 tons of water, were ready-made locations for helicopter pads; but most of the other ships had to be given extra pillared support, enough to resist a possible crash landing.

A fleet of tankers, 15 of them, sailed south to supply fuel for the ships engaged in Operation Corporate. Without them the Falklands Campaign would have ground to a halt in a very short time. All modified for refuelling at sea, they carried diesel fuel for the gas turbine engines, heavier fuel oil for the older ships and lubricating oil and anti-freeze for the machines and equipment ashore. Some were designated to carry fresh water, for although most of the Royal Navy ships had equipment for converting sea-water into fresh water, the merchant ships did not and there was insufficient fresh water available in the Falklands' area. The tankers often carried out their refuelling under conditions normally considered impossible. In one instance, when the frigate *Ambuscade* all but ran out of fuel, she was refuelled from astern by the tanker *British Esk* in a Force 10 gale. Although they were frequently bombed by Argentinian reconnaissance aircraft, not once during the whole of Operation Corporate did the converted tankers allow any ship to run out of fuel.

One by one merchant vessels were requisitioned and converted into repair ships, aircraft ferries (even a ten per cent loss of operational aircraft from *Hermes* and

A general map of the South Atlantic and the Total Exclusion Zone around the Falkland Islands.

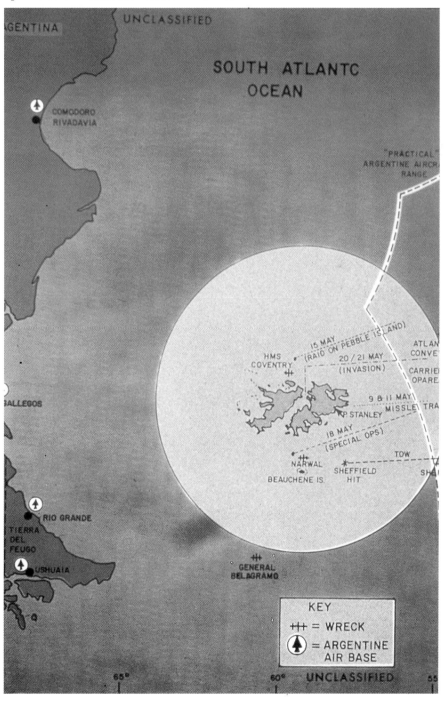

Invincible would have made it impossible to combat the strong Argentinian Air Force), tugs, dispatch vessels and hospital ships – and the transformations were often carried out with little or no warning. The *Stena Seaspread*, a 6,061-ton (6,-158-tonne) multi-purpose diving and surface support vessel, was taken up so quickly from her duties on a North Sea oil rig, that she sailed from Portsmouth and a four-day modification with a diver still in her decompression chamber. The transformation of the liner *Uganda* into a hospital ship in three days was a minor miracle. Requisitioned on 10 April in Alexandria harbour, the 16,907-ton (17,176-tonne) cruise liner had a thousand schoolchildren aboard on a normal Mediterranean educa-

tional cruise. Three days later they were disembarked at Naples, singing 'Rule Britainnia' as they trailed down the gangways, their holiday at an abrupt end. Impatiently a survey team of engineers waited to get aboard to carry out the redesign and preliminary conversions on the way to Gibraltar and a major conversion. Operating theatres, intensive care units, recovery rooms and general wards were created, together with the construction of a helicopter deck to take on possible casualties. She was also painted white with huge red crosses and registered as a hospital under the Geneva Convention. These and many other difficulties were rapidly overcome when the merchant fleet sailed for the Falklands.

The Threat Increases

The first few days when the task force lay off the Falklands produced a high number of false alarms, from air, surface and submarine sources as detection operators accustomed themselves to a war. This was further complicated by the wide dispersal of ships, the friendly air activity – helicopters were constantly either on ASW and surface searches or replenishing stores from merchantmen – and whales. Whales, which gave an alarmingly realistic contact, were frequently attacked with AS torpedoes in the early stage of the operation, until operators became able to recognize their slow, deliberate movement through the water.

Aircraft Attacks

On 1 May the returning ships entered the TEZ (Total Exclusion Zone) for the first time and joined the main force. It was a day of intense enemy air activity, with Argentinian Mirages and A4 Skyhawks coming in on hit-and-run attacks. Despite refuelling in the air, Argentine bombers from the mainland were at the full extent of their range and had only four or five minutes combat time over the targets, so the pilots needed to select their targets quickly and make an immediate run-in. They also needed fine weather and flying conditions for refuelling, selecting their targets and making their runs-in, so the task force looked for murky, overcast con-

HMS Hermes *and an escort in heavy seas during the Campaign. Without the Harriers from* Hermes *and* Invincible *and the air cover they provided, it would have been impossible to attempt the retaking of the Falklands.*

With the sinking of the Argentinian Belgrano, the pace of the war increased very quickly. Flying her Jolly Roger in recognition of her sinking the Belgrano, HMS Conqueror returns to her home base at Faslane.

ditions, viewing fine weather with the utmost apprehension. The dare-devil Argentinian pilots came in at low level, wherever possible out of the sun, skimming the sea. Hurtling in at 600 mph (960 km/h) the pilots had to react with split-second accuracy; in straight, level flight the bombs had to be released at exactly the right position to the target, the distance and height absolutely correct – too low and the bombs would skid along the surface or ricochet over the target. Throughout the Campaign, the Argentinian Air Force pushed home its attacks with fanatical zeal, regardless of losses. Seldom more than 50 per cent of their aircraft returned to the homeland and often whole sorties were wiped out.

The Loss of the *Sheffield*

A search was made on 2 May around the north of the island for the Argentinian submarine *San Luis* which had been reported in the area; results were negative. There was a tingle of expectancy in the air; the cruiser *Belgrano* and her destroyer group were somewhere to the south and the aircraft carrier *De Mayo* lay to the north. There was every likelihood of a surface attack from both directions. At 2300 hours the news came through that the British submarine *Conqueror* had detected and sunk the *Belgrano*, and that her attendant destroyers had turned tail and fled. The

The French-built Super Etendards with their deadly Exocet anti-ship missiles took a heavy toll of R.N. ships. Because of the lack of airborne early-warning radar, the ships only had a moment's warning of approaching enemy aircraft.

Force awaited the news of a similar attack on the *De Mayo*, but the carrier was never located despite air searches by Lynx, and the Argentine out-flanking movement was never put into operation. The sense of jubilation thoughout the Force turned to one of horror two days later when the *Sheffield* was hit by an Exocet missile fired from a French-made Etendard aircraft which had been beyond the ship's horizon and radar range. Hit amidships, the *Sheffield* was soon a mass of flames as her aluminium super-structure ignited. Ignoring the risk of further Exocets and explosions aboard the stricken ship, the *Arrow* went alongside to help fight the raging fires while a shuttle of cross-decking helicopters flew off the injured. With reluctance and only because the fire was out of control, the order was given to abandon ship and the survivors were flown to the *Arrow*. This was a sobering experience and brought home, in no uncertain manner, that Operation Corporate was no picnic, the Task Force really had a war on their hands.

Air attacks became a matter of routine. 'Zulu' time, Greenwich Mean Time, had been kept since the beginning of the operation, and gradually the 'body clocks' of the crews adjusted themselves to the 'unnatural' time sequence. Three hours ahead of the Argentinians they had already breakfasted and cleaned ship and got over that 'lowest ebb' well before the first wave of attacking aircraft came in. Shore bombardment of Argentinian positions around Port Stanley were carried out by a 22/42 combination. The Type 22 frigate acted as a close air defence to the 'Sheffield' class destroyers which carried out the shelling with 4.5-inch automatic guns – it was at this point that it was realized what a blessing it would have been if the Type 22 had also carried a similar gun.

The jubilation that had been raised for the sinking of the Belgrano faded very quickly when HMS Sheffield was hit by an Exocet missile. The missile had come in so quickly that, at first, it was thought that Sheffield had been hit by a torpedo.

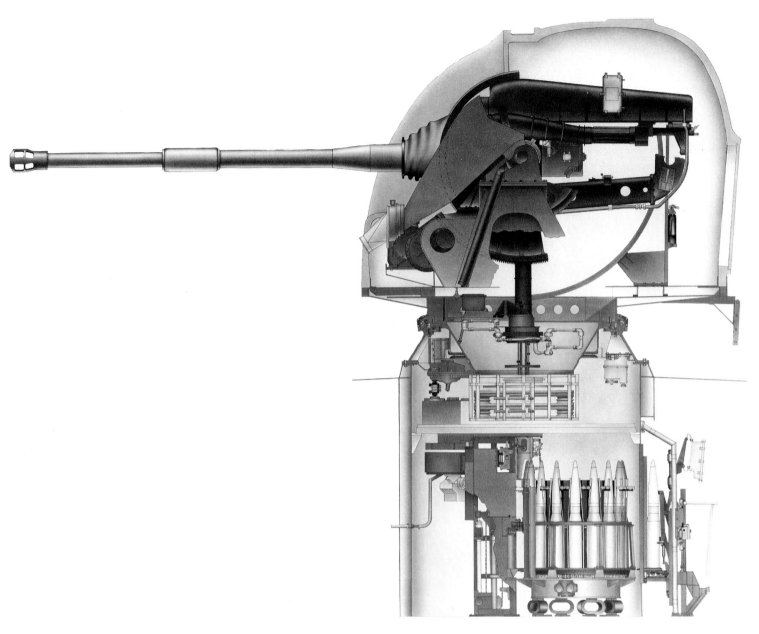

A cut-away of the Vickers 4.5-in Mk 8 fully automatic gun. It was used to provide support for the land forces creeping close in shore to bombard enemy positions.

Opposite: A Sea Wolf missile is loaded into its firing tube. The Sea Wolf provided a very effective defensive system against low-level air threats but not enough ships were fitted with it.

Overleaf: A Navy Sea King silhouetted against the setting sun. The pilots flew many more missions than had been expected and fatigue took a heavy toll on the crews.

At 1630 on 12 May, while running a gun line south of the Port Stanley minefields, *Brilliant* and *Glasgow* spotted four enemy planes tracking fast overland to the east along the coast. The Sea Wolf radar locked on perfectly as the Skyhawks turned to come screaming in for the attack, out of the sun, at sea level. The Sea Wolf system engaged the enemy automatically, and 'hands off' selected the optimum range and fired. The first two Skyhawks were taken out in rapid succession; the third crashed into the sea taking avoiding action. The fourth got his bombs away, but too late and they passed harmlessly over *Brilliant* – this aircraft was shot down by its own forces as it flew over the land.

Confidently *Brilliant* awaited the second attack by Argentinian aircraft. It came half an hour later, out of the sun, from the same direction – four more Skyhawks. To the consternation of the British operators, the Sea Wolf radar generated clutter tracks and the weapons system failed to lock-on to any of the incoming raid. Banging away with 40-mm Bofors AA guns and 20-mm Oerlikons, chattering GPMGs (General Purpose Machine Guns) and LMGs (Light Machine Guns), *Brilliant* and *Glasgow* were helpless as the bombs began to fall. As luck had it, the bombs aimed at *Brilliant* bounced over the bows, through the masts and across the flight-deck aft. The *Glasgow*, not so lucky, took a bouncing bomb through the after-machinery space, but it went clear through and out the other side without exploding. Sobered by this experience, *Brilliant* shepherded *Glasgow* away from the coast to carry out temporary repairs and rejoin the Force.

Aboard *Brilliant*, David Breen, the Marconi engineer, who had foreseen the possibility of a Sea Wolf failure early in Springtrain, signalled the information to

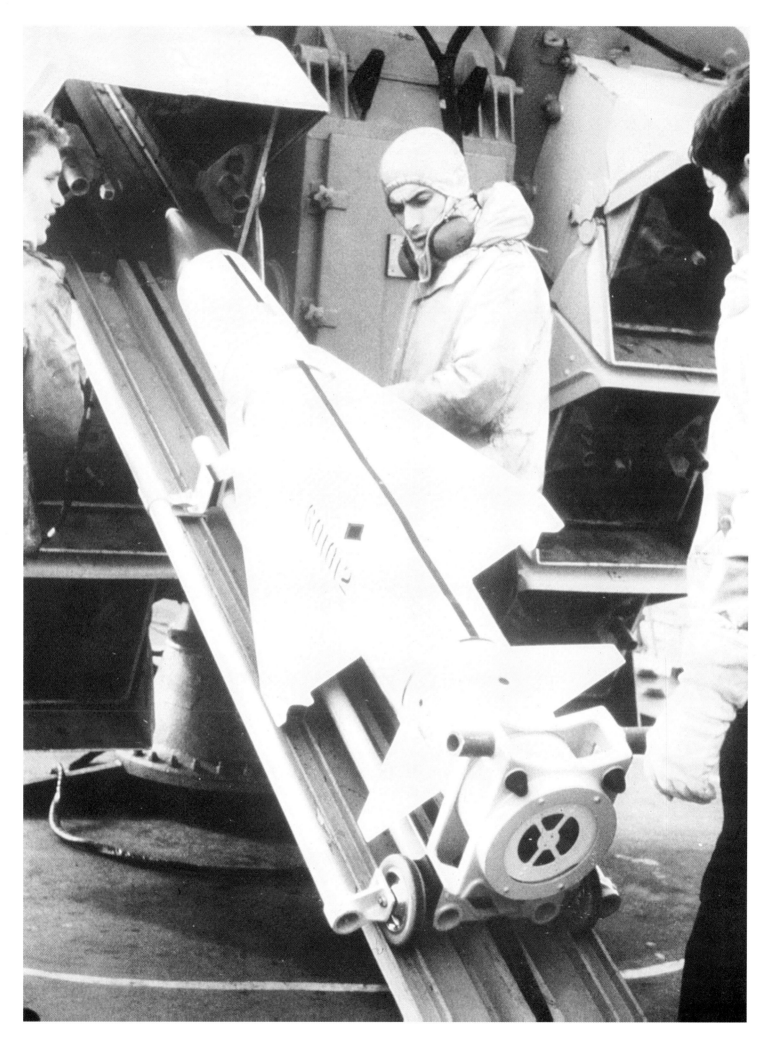

the Weapons Establishment at Portsmouth in England. Working 24 hours a day, engineers solved the problem, tested out their findings with aircraft, and signalled back the information within 48 hours.

Helicopter Accidents

All did not go well with the helicopter flights; the sheer volume of air traffic and the number of hours being flown presupposed accidents. At 0200 hours on 18 May a Sea King helicopter with four occupants ditched but they were successfully rescued by another aircraft. The following night a far more serious accident occurred. It was a black, bitterly cold night as a Sea King, carrying 27 SAS members and a crew of three, turned downwind to circuit before landing on the assault ship *Intrepid*. For little apparent reason the aircraft hit the water and the tail section broke away. The helicopter sank immediately, taking down 20 of the 30 men with her. The remaining ten struggled in the freezing water until one was winched aboard another Sea King; the others were rescued by a Pacific Searider. The icy sea had been too much for one who was dead on arrival aboard *Brilliant*. The other eight, all suffering from hypothermia, were hurried under hot showers and pummelled to keep them breathing – it was touch and go with one or two, but all survived.

The British Invasion

At midnight on 20 May the invasion convoy headed into the islands, escorting the main landing force. The destination was San Carlos Water off the Falkland Sound, which was to become known as 'Bomb Alley' to the British. The escort ships, frigates and destroyers positioned themselves around the merchantmen, offering an umbrella of air defence in the event of an Argentinian air attack; and come it did – fast and furious sorties were flown as the enemy tried to forestall the landings. Hugging the shore of San Carlos Water, the defence became almost like a Second World War battle in which Bofors, Oerlikons and GMPGs were used for air protection – clutter from the surrounding hills made radar interception difficult.

At 1050 hours GMT, in the half-light of a Falkland's dawn, men, machinery and equipment were being ferried ashore by

Opposite: A Lynx helicopter from HMS Abuscade delivers urgently needed supplies to the Royal Fleet Auxiliary Plumleaf.

Overleaf: A painting, especially commissioned by P & O, of the Canberra, the 'Great White Whale', as she disembarks 3 Commando at San Carlos Water.

The heaviest air and naval fighting was at San Carlos Water, as the land forces established a secure land base for the push on Stanley.

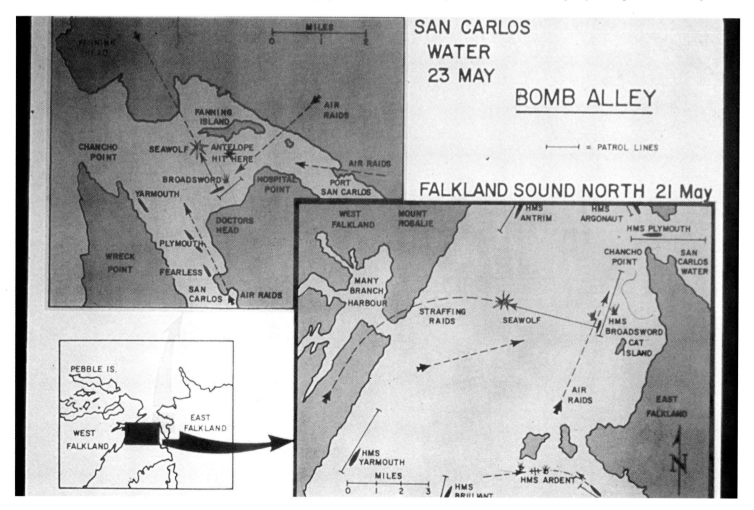

helicopter from the supply ships huddled off the eastern shore of San Carlos. Beyond, in the Sound, Type 22 frigates provided advanced cover and aircraft warning. A light wind barely ruffled the waters of the bay, which remained calm in all but the roughest weather – in the light of the dramatic weather changes in the Falkland's area, which had been a major consideration in the choice of beach-head. Lying at the western end of the main island, San Carlos Water was a narrow strip of water surrounded by a defensive ring of hills which offered maximum protection against air attack. Pilots flying in over the hills at 600 mph (960 km/h) would have just seconds in which to choose a target and make their bombing run.

Anxiously the crews peered up at the clearing skies; it looked like being a fine, sunny day, just the weather for Argentinian air attacks. Flying in low to avoid

detection, the 'map of the earth' technique, and hugging the contours of the ground, a Wessex V flew past making for the shore, a heavy load swinging below; others were criss-crossing with Land Rovers, Rapier missiles, ammunition and food. The warships, at action stations, waited tensely for the coming attacks. The morning passed but still there were no Argentinian attacks; the midday meal, a bowl of soup and a great hunk of bread, were brought to men closed at their action stations aboard a Type 21 frigate, sheltered as close inshore as possible without actually going aground. Protected from the east by the steep cliffs, she would be able to concentrate her fire on enemy aircraft coming across from the west, or ahead and astern down the length of San Carlos.

With the imminent possibility of radar clutter, the coming air battles were unlikely to be fought from the operations

Task Force ships at San Carlos Water before disembarking, as the landing craft scurry between the ships and the shore. The risk of air attack was ever-present.

room, so the Principal Weapons Officer (Air) was posted on the Gun Direction Position above the bridge. With the aircraft coming in low the ship would have to be fought visually, from advanced information received from the Sound. That came at 1310; one siren after another wailed out; the incoming Argentine aircraft had been spotted. The Action gong clanged throughout the ship and over the intercom came 'Air raid warning – Red'. At 'Enemy aircraft sighted in Sound – look out West', the LAZ sight operator swung his binoculars around in that direction, the 4.5-inch gun automatically following. Around the bridge the look-outs and other hands on the upper deck pointed their weapons to the west, and a motley collection they were – machine guns, rifles, 'very' light pistols, a row of distress rockets clamped to a makeshift wooden board, smoke grenades, anything that might distract an incoming pilot for that fraction of a second, so vital for an assured hit. The 20-mm Oerlikon gunner, strapped to his seat, kicked himself round to face west.

'Aircraft sighted, bearing Red five zero', sang out the PWO (A). The scream of engines shattered the peace as four enemy Mirages swooped over the brow of the hill across Falkland Sound, diving for the ships in San Carlos Water ('Death Valley' as it became known to the Argentinians). Pursuing Sea Harriers peeled off left and right at the crest of the hills to avoid being caught in the AA crossfire. The defending warships opened up with everything, a deadly crossfire of missiles, 4.5-inch shells, 20-mm cannon, with here and there the green trail of a very light flare – one overenthusiastic loader was throwing empty 20-mm shell cases and expletives. The Oerlikon pumped away at 3,000 ft (900 m) – closing – then swung himself around to follow the departing Mirages. A bomb, released too low, ricocheting like a skimming stone across the water, streaked just feet beyond the frigate's bows; another exploded harmlessly as it hit the sea. A Mirage went up in a ball of flame – everyone claimed the hit. The other three vanished over the hills, one followed by a heat-seeking Rapier missile from ashore; a sudden flash of light registered a hit. 'Aircraft departing' but no one relaxed.

Less than a minute later, the two remaining Mirages were coming in again, 20-mm cannon spitting, up the Bay across

The Antelope *pours smoke after being hit by bombs. She had been attacked by four Skyhawks. A Sea Cat missile got one Skyhawk and another was hit by 20-mm gunfire, but it was at this moment that she was hit by two 1,000-lb (454-kg) bombs.*

HMS Yarmouth *closes in alongside the stricken HMS Ardent.* She had been hit during the last air raid of the day, by several 1,000-lb (454-kg) bombs and there was no chance of saving her.

the ships, then heading for home, one of them spewing smoke and unlikely to make it. With scarcely a break the next raid was on them, this time four A4 Skyhawks. Two never reached San Carlos Water as they were taken out by Sea Wolf missiles. The others dropped their bombs, missed and turned for home. With fanatical zeal the Argentinian airmen pressed home their attacks over the next few days with crippling, insurmountable losses.

Against such frenzied attacks there just had to be some British losses. The *Antrim* was hit by a bomb that failed to expode. The Type 21 frigate *Antelope* was also hit but without *Antrim*'s luck. Hit by two bombs, she crawled up the bay, gaping holes in her hull, her mainmast slanted at a

A *huge cloud of smoke hangs over the landing ship* Sir Galahad, *after she had been hit by Mirage and Skyhawk aircraft.*

crazy angle and with one of the bombs, unexploded, still inside her. After dark, in the Sound, she went up, scattering flaming debris high into the air. Burning red-hot throughout the night, she finally slipped under the following day. On 25 May, the Argentinians came in strength. *Coventry* and *Broadsword* were hit and the *Coventry* sunk soon after. *Brilliant*, 'goal-keeping'

alongside *Hermes*, picked up two Exocets coming in close together and ordered the Sea Wolf locked-on ready to take them out. Suddenly the Exocets made a dramatic 30-degree turn towards a cloud of chaff fired by a Type 21 frigate. The Sea Wolf system followed them until it reached its 'self-protection' point; then it stopped. With growing horror the operators watched the missiles remorselessly on target for the *Atlantic Conveyor*. Unfortunately, nothing could be done, for almost simultaneously the Exocets crashed into the after-section of the ship. Although 24 crew members were picked up from the icy sea by frigates, sadly the captain of the *Atlantic Conveyor* was lost.

Disaster struck on 8 June when the LSLs (Landing Ship Logistic) *Sir Galahad* and *Sir Tristram* were attacked at Fitzroy. At 1310 hours two Mirages and two Skyhawks streaked across the unguarded bay and caught the two ships as the *Sir Galahad* was being unloaded. There was no effective anti-aircraft fire and both ships received direct hits. *Sir Galahad* was carrying men of the Welsh Guards and a mixed cargo. A bomb hit a consignment of petrol for the Rapier generators and turned the ship into an inferno.

It was all over by Tuesday 15 June. Argentina surrendered and most of the naval officers and men returned to their home ports in the United Kingdom. Many of them had been at sea for over 100 days. Many lessons had been learned from the Falklands Campaign and the Royal Navy emerged from it a wiser and more efficient fighting unit.

The Canberra returns home to the cheers of the waiting crowds. The Navy requisitioned a total of 54 merchant ships of all types from 33 companies. The Merchant Navy would have a vital role to play in any other major war.

Admiral Woodward's flagship, HMS Hermes, returns to a hero's welcome. The Task Force had lost six ships and 10 others had sustained damage. The Hermes is now kept in reserve at Portsmouth.

INDEX